LIVING BEAUTIFULLY

Creating a Holistic Lifestyle

Denise Dubois

LIVING BEAUTIFULLY

ISBN 978-0-578-66946-5

DEDICATION

I dedicate this book to the many mentors and teachers who have inspired and encouraged me, and to my family and friends who have supported me over the years. I am especially grateful to my sons, Paul and Thomas for pushing me to do my best, my mom and dad for their constant support, and my husband, Bill for always listening to my ideas and encouraging me to continue. Special acknowledgment and with great gratitude to Sarah Falcon for her many contributions to helping this book take shape.

"Love yourself enough to live a healthy lifestyle."

Dr. Shaunna Menard

TABLE OF CONTENTS

FOREWORD

I have had the pleasure of knowing Denise Dubois for over 20 years and as a consummate professional, tireless student of life, and a cherished friend. As a fellow esthetics professional, we share a passion in educating and treating others.

My background is in professional esthetics, technical education, and developing new skin therapies. I've worked with dermatologists, plastic surgeons, and cosmetic chemists to co-develop highly effective skincare. As Denise is as well, I'm an educator – working with clients to bring cutting-edge corrective techniques and holistic information about skin health and aging.

In this capacity, I am constantly reading and searching for new nuggets of wisdom and information. There is no shortage – for better or worse – of books about health maintenance, graceful aging, and beauty. What stands out in Denise's approach is the patience and care she brings to this book.

In a world of short cuts and quick fixes, *Living Beautifully: Creating A Holistic Lifestyle* is a refreshingly inspired work and approach to improving one's life and the experience of living.

Rather than a hard-driven case for following a specific (and ultimately unrealistic) plan, Denise encapsulates health-promoting techniques into compact and manageable methods that are, in themselves, singularly beneficial for the reader. Since we all know that any effort invested in smart lifestyle practices is superior to none at all, the simple-to-understand and use examples found here may make personal improvement more likely. The information is timeless and especially useful in our busy world.

Denise writes from the heart and first-hand experience. Her experience, expertise, and thoughtfulness shine through. I hope this book brings you as much value and pleasure as it did for me.

Warmest regards,

Douglas Preston

INTRODUCTION

This book has been on my mind for a long time and has been several years in the making. It's a compilation of all I've learned from mentors, educators, books, study, and client interactions. As I created a holistic lifestyle for myself, the seeds of this book began to grow.

Running a spa may be the opposite of a holistic lifestyle — it requires constant care and attention to others (both guests of the spa and employees) and there are always hundreds of balls in the air. For me to live my best life and foster my health, my relationships, and my wellbeing, I have found a few key things that serve me and our clients well. They include consistent exercise, daily fresh air in our beautiful surroundings, making time for friends and family, and building regular nurturing rituals.

It's not just me who is living a stress-filled life. When I meet with a spa client and discuss their wellness and skincare goals, I ask for background on their lifestyle. All of our everyday stresses, joys, nutrition, and exercise show in our faces and affect how we feel. We know that acne, for example, can be a symptom of an imbalanced life, rather than a condition. Without understanding the root causes and addressing them, what we do in our spas is, frankly, just skin deep.

In recent years, when I ask my clients to rate their stress levels from one to 10, the answers I usually get are high: reaching seven, eight, and nine. This level of chronic stress that so many of us are carrying has enormous impacts on our skin, our bodies, our happiness, and our health. Simply asking the question can bring out emotional reactions.

This book is intended to help you counteract the emotional and environmental tolls our modern life takes. I am here to be your helping hand and show you what a holistic lifestyle could look like for you, and why it can bring balance, joy, beauty, and wellness to your life.

Yours in health,

Denise

Denise Dubois

THE HOLISTIC LIFESTYLE

For me, a holistic lifestyle is a daily way of living that extends the benefits of the spa beyond its four walls. Our spas are set in upstate New York, a place with strong connections to nature, wellness, and healing. Saratoga Springs — a city with several mineral springs where one of our spas is located — is known for its healing waters and has been a historical destination for health seekers.

Some say that Saratoga is a mispronunciation of the Mohawk tribe word "Serachtuague," which means "place of fast-moving water." Mohawk and Iroquois tribes went to the springs for drinking and bathing, taking in the waters' healing and curative properties. George Washington advocated the springs' healing powers, and by the 19th century, Saratoga was considered "the Queen of Spas."

Spas around the world have been places for health and healing. In many cultures, spa visits were done occasionally as treatments for specific issues but were also made part of an overall healthy lifestyle. While visiting a spa can be an important part of a healthy lifestyle, it can't replace the huge benefits of daily care. I think that a holistic lifestyle, where every day is imbued with choices centered around your health and wellbeing, is a beautiful way to live.

MY STORY

As a young teenager, I suffered from acne and sought the care of a dermatologist. There, I was treated like everyone else was during those times — with antibiotics and trichloroacetic acid (TCA) chemical peels. This standard treatment didn't address the root cause of my acne or how diet could be impacting the condition of my skin. It only addressed the superficial symptoms. The stress I felt as a result of my acne certainly could have been contributing to and exacerbating the symptoms and were absolutely affecting my self-esteem.

I became interested in learning makeup application and began my career in the beauty industry as a makeup artist. I soon realized that makeup was only camouflaging the symptoms of what was going on internally. That inspired me to go to esthetics school to learn the science behind the health of my skin and how to properly treat it for optimal results. There I learned how healthy skin is beautiful, and that makeup should enhance it, rather than mask an unhealthy complexion.

As my knowledge grew, I realized I couldn't only treat the skin on the surface. The skin is a reflection of what is going on inside the mind and body. I began thinking about how to treat the body as a whole system, rather than just looking at the isolated skin conditions. After first graduating from make-up designer school in New York City, and then cosmetology school followed by esthetics school, I worked in a hair salon. At the time, there wasn't yet a concept of a "day spa" in the United States, and so the only option was a room in the back of a hair salon. There, I performed facials, skin treatments, and applied makeup. After three years, I left the salon environment and founded the first of my spas, Complexions Professional Skin Care, in Albany, New York with my self and one other employee. I continued my training and education over the years and achieved my CIDESCO diploma, as well as certification as a wellness coach, and in nutritional skincare. The spa evolved and grew into Complexions Spa for Beauty and Wellness. From there I went on to open a second spa location in Saratoga Springs, where I now spend my time between the two locations and manage an amazing team of dedicated spa professionals.

In the 35-plus years of working as a professional esthetician, I have seen hundreds of clients at the spa and through my husband's cosmetic surgery practice. There, I worked with patients both pre- and post-operatively to help optimize their surgical results, reduce healing time, and improve the health and condition of their skin.

I wanted to make sure to give each person what I hadn't received as a teenager with acne: a thoughtful, holistic approach to skincare. Our spas offer a comprehensive look at overall health. We develop client profiles that aren't just about addressing the superficial skin conditions but creating a long-term program for overall skin health and beauty.

As I age, as we all do, I have become personally more and more interested in understanding how my lifestyle choices impact my overall health, wellbeing, and appearance. You might think that now is the time to bring out the "big guns" — the strongest products and toughest technologies.

The more I see in my practice, the more I study, and the more I see in my personal life, I realize that it is the gentler, persistent, cleaner, and more holistic products and practices that have the best, long-term impacts on health and beauty. In fact, the "big gun" approach can lead to skin that ages more quickly and doesn't set a person up for healthier skin longterm.

What I've discovered for myself is that a combination of daily wellness practices, impactful and clean products, and regular professional care is the best path for aging well and living beautifully.

WHY IT'S HARD TO LIVE DAILY WELLNESS

Daily wellness, of course, is easier said than done. In our everyday lives, we are bombarded with distractions from healthy choices. Our phones are constant sources of stress, diversion, work, and frustration. While there is more food than ever, processed foods and fast "healthy" foods still don't replace healthy, organic fruits, vegetables, and clean proteins.

We know we should disconnect to reconnect with our environment and loved ones, but work expectations of being always "on-call" and the very addictive design of our smartphones make it very difficult to do. Whew! No wonder we feel so stressed!

CREATING A HOLISTIC LIFESTYLE

This book isn't about quick fixes or hard rules. I'm not promising you'll lose seven pounds in seven days. Instead, it's a different way of thinking about how each part of your life can add value. It's not a simple solution because, as we've learned over time, human wellness is far more complicated than just our physical health. It's a complex interaction between physical, mental, spiritual, and emotional health.

Being unwell isn't merely a symptom of physical imbalance, it is a reflection of the state of our entire being. We need to practice root cause analysis for ourselves to understand our personal balance of health and wellbeing. When you look at each component, how are you doing?

Look at the eight components that I have found are crucial to creating a holistic lifestyle. These are nutritious eating, physical activity, fresh air and nature, relationships, work, de-stressing, self-care, and professional treatments. In the next chapters, I will go deeper into how each component can be a valuable and positive force in your life.

Before we start, take a few minutes to do a quick self-assessment on how your current lifestyle is serving you. Based on our eight key components, you can create a map of your overall wellbeing.

HOLISTIC SELF-ASSESSMENT

See the example below and then do the following steps on the clean diagram provided on the following page:

1. Place a dot on the line to indicate how happy you are in each area. A dot towards the center (0) reflects dissatisfaction, a dot towards the periphery (100) indicates satisfaction

2. Connect the dots to see your holistic wellbeing assessment

3. Identify the imbalances and see where to spend your energy to create more balance

The results may look like this:

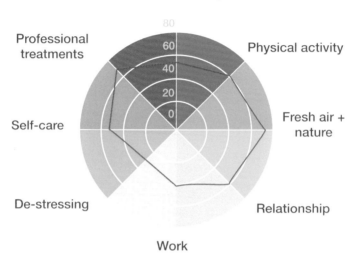

Use this diagram below. To download a printable PDF, please visit: duboisbeauty.com/pages/living-beautifully

This book is designed to help you understand how you can move toward the outer edges of each component. In it, you'll find deep dives into science and understanding, quick tips that you can start today, routines that you can incorporate for yourself over time, and quotes that bring me joy and peace. I hope that this can be a starting point for you to begin owning and creating your holistic lifestyle. I look forward to sharing this journey with you.

NUTRITIOUS EATING

I start with nutrition. It's a cornerstone of health and pleasure and contributes to your overall wellbeing. Always opt for the highest quality, delicious, clean food products that are fresh, local, in season, and organic whenever possible. Meals can become small rituals of self-care.

What we eat shows on our skin. The skin is the largest organ of the body and it reflects what is going on internally. What you eat and drink, along with other lifestyle choices, greatly impacts your skin's appearance. Skincare products and professional treatments alone can only achieve so much. Beauty must be approached holistically, and nutrition and skincare must be done simultaneously to achieve desired results.

For clients struggling with dry, acneic, sensitive, and depleted skin, I look to diet and lifestyle for potential triggers and for opportunities to make meaningful suggestions. For example, dairy and sugar can be sources of acneic outbreaks; not drinking enough water can cause dry, dehydrated skin; food sensitivities can show as red or irritated skin, including eczema and psoriasis.

In this chapter, I'll talk about some of the key components of nutritious eating for skin health and overall wellbeing: clean eating, gut health, macronutrients and micronutrients, water, and journaling.

"What most people don't realize is that food is not just calories; it's information. It actually contains messages that connect to every cell in the body."
– Dr. Mark Hyman

WHAT IS CLEAN EATING?

"Clean eating" has become more and more popular as people gain knowledge and become more aware of the consequences of food choices. But rather than being a new phenomenon, it gets us back to our roots of eating whole, non-processed, seasonal, and nutritious foods that are as close to their source as possible.

There are many different definitions of what "clean" means, but for me, it means avoiding processed foods, sugars, and refined carbohydrates (such as white rice and white flour); minimal dairy, and select animal protein. I also like to map out my meals for the week on Sundays, so I am prepared, leaving me less likely to scramble at the last moment and make poor choices.

Rather than looking at eating clean as restricting choices, I have found that clean eating is an opportunity to try new things and enjoy the health benefits of nutrient and vitamin-rich, satiating, and delicious foods.

INFLAMMATION

There is a lot of talk about inflammation today and how all diseases can be traced back to inflammatory imbalances. What exactly is inflammation? Inflammation is the body's natural response to protect itself against harm.

Inflammation is caused by three primary triggers:

- wounds or trauma

- microbial invasion

- nutrition and diet

There are two types of inflammation: acute and chronic. The food choices we make can help control inflammation. Too little of an inflammatory response can lead to slow wound healing and thriving microbes in the body. Too much inflammation and the body begins to attack itself, leading to chronic disease. We must do our best to try and keep ourselves in balance.

You're probably more familiar with the acute type of inflammation, which occurs when you injure yourself. Your immune system triggers an army of white blood cells to surround and protect the area where the injury occurred, creating visible redness and swelling.

The process works similarly if you have an infection like the flu or bronchitis. In these examples, inflammation is essential— without it, injuries could fester and simple infections could be deadly. Inflammation keeps us alive. It's when the inflammation becomes chronic that it is thought to be an underlying factor linked to diseases such as cancer, heart disease, diabetes, Alzheimer's, allergies, asthma, weight gain, and accelerated aging.

When there is a trigger, the inflammatory response to correct things is called the "initiation response." Once things are resolved, there is a "resolution response" which shuts off the inflammatory reaction. It is when this does not occur that inflammation turns to cellular inflammation, leading to chronic disease.

Our best line of defense against cellular inflammation is consuming a healthy and whole diet that is balanced with low-fat proteins and plant-based carbohydrates.

- Avoid: Omega 6 fatty acids like vegetable oils, saturated fats, and excess amounts of carbohydrates from grains, starches, and sugar
- Increase: Omega 3 from fish, and polyphenols from fruits and vegetables

This will look very similar to the Mediterranean diet. As you can see, an unhealthy diet and lifestyle choices can make us sick.

*"Let food be your medicine and
medicine be your food."*
— Hippocrates

GUT HEALTH: THE IMPORTANCE OF A HEALTHY GUT AND WHAT YOU NEED TO KNOW

Some of our body's most important players are found in the gut. About 80% of the body's immune system resides in the lining of it, and 70% of our white blood cells are found there. Hippocrates, traditionally regarded as the father of medicine, said that all disease begins in the gut, which is why we must focus on what we choose to eat.

THE GUT AND ITS RESPONSIBILITIES

The gut, or gastrointestinal passage, includes the small intestine and large intestine. The small intestine is long and narrow and averages about 7 meters (23 feet) long. The large intestine is wider in diameter but shorter than the small intestine at about 1.5 meters (5 feet) long.

During the last few years, there has been an increased awareness of maintaining good gut health. The gut makes up the largest colonies of microbes in the human body, with the average adult carrying up to 2 kilograms of bacteria. These microorganisms, consisting mostly of bacteria, fungi, viruses, and yeast, form a living fabric of controls that affects our mood, weight, nutrition, and immunity.

These bacteria have several key responsibilities that aid in maintaining our bodies. These include helping to process food, metabolize bile acids, sterols, and xenobiotics. They also help support digestion, influence gut motility, and fight disease while balancing out hormone levels, vitamin levels, and neurotransmitters.

LIFESTYLE AND DIET

Our lifestyle and diet play major roles in the diversity of our gut; when our gut microbiota is disrupted, our immunity is reduced, making our bodies susceptible to diseases and disorders. Things that can impact our gut health include:

- high sugar intake
- processed foods
- synthetic fats
- antibiotics
- unclean water
- pesticides
- persistent organic pollutants such as PCP's
- heavy metals
- antibacterial soap
- stress and lack of sleep

These factors play a direct role in creating inflammatory skin conditions like acne, rosacea, psoriasis, and eczema, and can contribute to aging and glycation or flares in autoimmune diseases.

HOW TO IMPROVE YOUR GUT HEALTH

Overwhelmed yet? Don't be! While this information may make good gut health seem almost impossible, there are easy changes we can make. The first step to a healthier gut is eliminating foods that cause inflammation.

Junk food, sugary treats, processed foods, and foods that contain artificial sweeteners or refined carbohydrates should be drastically cut from our everyday diet. Additionally, gluten, dairy, and even shellfish (which is high in iodine) can trigger acne, so these foods should also be eaten in moderation. Choosing gluten-free and dairy-free alternatives can help make this lifestyle change easier for you and your family. When I simply cut out creamer in my coffee and switched to coconut milk I experiences huge changes with how I felt.

Drinking bone broth — a rich liquid made from animal bones (and often herbs, vegetables, and spices) — and/or collagen can help repair our gut lining and flora. Bone broth can also help repair any potential leaking in the lining. Having the right levels of acid in your stomach is important for digestive health as well.

QUICK TIPS TO ADD
GUT HEALTH FOODS

Add gut-health supporting foods to your diet to help boost your skin health and overall wellbeing.

- Remove inflammatory foods like sugar and white flour

- Moderately consume caffeine and alcohol

- Drink 1-2 tablespoons of apple cider vinegar diluted with water 30 minutes before eating to help stimulate digestive enzymes

- Squeeze half a lemon into the water to aid digestive health and reduce inflammation

- Add probiotic foods like yogurt, kombucha, and pickled vegetables help populate good bacteria

- Choose prebiotic foods like cabbage, broccoli, avocado, and sweet potatoes help feed good gut bacteria

These gut-health supporting foods and liquids help improve the functioning of the microbiota while allowing the growth and activity of good bacteria, which lives throughout the gut and keep you healthy. There's also a beauty benefit: these items can improve the lipid barrier and the skin's immune system.

It is also possible and often needed, to do a cleansing diet for three weeks eliminating gluten, eggs, dairy, soy, and sugar. Then slowly reintroduce each food with a few days in between each one. Watch how your body responds and proceed carefully.

See what foods or beverages trigger headaches, bloating, discomfort, stomach aches, or lethargy. When do you feel most balanced, energetic, and comfortable? Mindfully eating, and carefully monitoring of your body's responses can be your best guide. You may even want to keep a daily food journal to notice any patterns.

NUTRIENT-RICH FOOD CHOICES

Nutrients are defined as "a substance that provides nourishment essential for growth and the maintenance of life." It comes from the Latin word *nutrient* meaning "nourishing." Thinking about food from a nutrient-based perspective offers a thoughtful way of looking at food choices.

For example, building a diet around nutrient-rich foods that satisfy a macronutrient balance and that work for you, and trying different foods with a variety of micronutrients, can be a healthy and enjoyable way to eat and experience new foods.

Nutrition experts have divided nutrients — things like proteins, fats, vitamins, and minerals — into two categories:

- Macronutrients are nutrients your body needs in large quantities. These are fats, proteins, and carbohydrates.

- Micronutrients are nutrients your body needs in smaller quantities. These are vitamins and minerals.

MACRONUTRIENTS

Macronutrients are divided into three categories: fats, proteins, and carbohydrates. Each one is needed in large amounts to support your health and wellbeing. Nutritionists recommend balancing your macronutrient intake, with a mix of each.

Everyone has their own specific individual needs that vary from one person to the next.

Carbohydrates

Carbohydrates provide the body with energy. Carbohydrates are small chains of sugar molecules that break down into glucose. Nutritionists recommend that carbohydrates make up about 35-65% of your diet. Healthy carbohydrates include whole grains, root vegetables, leafy greens, and fiber-rich fruits like apples, pears, and bananas.

Fat

Fat is critical for your overall health, as it supports brain development, overall cell function, organ protection, and vitamin absorption. It has also been shown to lower the risk of heart disease and stroke. Nutritionists recommend that fat makes up 20-35% of your food consumption. Healthy fats include oils (coconut), avocados, nuts, and eggs.

Protein

Protein helps support a healthy immune system, repair and regenerate tissues and cells, and manufacture hormones. When you eat protein, it is broken down into amino acids, which help build muscle and regular immune function. Nutritionists recommend 10-35% of your diet should come from protein. Healthy proteins include nuts, seeds, legumes, olives, avocados, fatty fish, and eggs.

MICRONUTRIENTS

Micronutrients are essential vitamins, minerals, and biochemicals our bodies need for proper growth and function. They help us produce energy and support all of the vital processes that occur in our bodies. They help ensure that things like our brain, immune system, muscles, bones, heart, and skin —among many other parts of our body — are working well and protecting our overall health.

We must obtain micronutrients from quality foods because our bodies cannot produce them. Therefore, when we pack our meals with nutrient-dense food, the micronutrients we consume can improve our health and our skin by providing vital vitamins and minerals that are crucial for our body's ability to function at its best.

The greatest source of micronutrients comes from high-quality whole grains, proteins, fruits, and vegetables. Eating healthy meals that incorporate foods with essential micronutrients is the best way to fuel your body. The powerful antioxidant benefits may even help our bodies fight disease, some cancers, Alzheimer's, and heart disease.

Quick Tips to Incorporate Micronutrients

Fuel your body and enhance your meals with micronutrient-rich, wholesome foods packed with vitamins and trace elements such as iron, zinc, fluoride, selenium, copper, chromium, iodine, and manganese.

- Eat greens at every meal. Add spinach to eggs, try a collard green wrap sandwich, add cabbage in a stir-fry.

- Snack on nuts and seeds. Look for ones that are organic, raw, and free of sugars and fillers like palm oils.

- Sweeten your plate with berries. They are antioxidant-rich and anti-inflammatory. Look for organic berries, since conventional ones (especially strawberries) can have a high level of pesticides.

- Batch cook whole grains, which are rich in vitamin B, iron, magnesium, and selenium. Amaranth, buckwheat, wild rice, oats, millet, and barley are delicious whole grains.

- Stock your pantry with legumes (including beans, peas, and lentils) and add them to salads, soups, and even smoothies.

THE IMPORTANCE OF WATER

I couldn't end this chapter without speaking about the importance of consuming water. Water is a cornerstone of health and wellbeing. Water supports your body's core functions, including digestion, circulation, and temperature regulation.

Replenishing with water during the day and when exercising helps you stay alert, energized, and performing at your best level. Plus, there are visible benefits: well-hydrated skin looks smoother, plumper, and younger.

Filtered tap water is an easy source. Add sliced fruits, vegetables, and herbs for a lightly-flavored (spa) beverage. Try caffeine-free herbal teas (hot or cold) and seltzers if you are looking for a change. Water-rich foods like watermelon, strawberries, cucumbers, and tomatoes can also keep you replenished and hydrated.

THE DIRTY DOZEN AND THE CLEAN FIFTEEN

Every year, the Environmental Working Group reviews pesticide levels in produce. Their findings help inform shoppers on where to focus their spending. The Dirty Dozen are produce found to have high levels of pesticides, so care should be taken when purchasing those products.

When possible, look for organic products, since those will have lower levels, or no traces of, pesticides. The Clean Fifteen are produce found to have the lowest traces of pesticides.

The Dirty Dozen	The Clean Fifteen
Strawberries	Avocados
Spinach	Sweet corn
Kale	Pineapples
Nectarines	Frozen sweet peas
Apples	Onions
Grapes	Papayas
Peaches	Eggplants
Cherries	Asparagus
Pears	Kiwis
Tomatoes	Cabbages
Celery	Cauliflower
Potatoes	Cantaloupes
	Broccoli
	Mushrooms
	Honeydew melons

FOOD JOURNALING

Food journaling is simply tracking the food you eat during the course of the day. There are several apps available that allow you to track the foods you eat. As you move towards building a diet based on healthier food choices that promote gut health, reduce inflammation and support your body with a mix of macronutrients and micronutrients, a journal can help you track your progress. Some people use an app to track calories and find it to be helpful. For others, simply writing down (or capturing on your phone) what you've eaten and how much can help change your relationship with the food you eat.

MINDFUL EATING

Mindful eating is the practice of eating with attention to (and not judgment of) the food we are ingesting. Rather than eating in front of the television, or while working, or quickly and thoughtlessly, mindful eating requires that we slow down and notice the physical and emotional experience of eating. Practitioners find that when they eat more slowly and mindfully, they can better understand their feelings of hunger and fullness. Awareness lets you stop when you are full and satisfied.

PHYSICAL ACTIVITY

Physical activity is a movement that requires the use of your muscles and burns energy and calories. There are many types of exercise and finding a style of exercise that fits your body, lifestyle, and health goals is the key to success. Before beginning an exercise regimen or making significant changes to your exercise routine, consult a doctor to ensure that the exercise is safe and appropriate for you and your individual needs.

Exercise has many benefits beyond improving health. Decades of scientific research support that burning 700 to 1,000 calories per week through physical activity can have a wide range of positive impacts. These include reduced risk of developing diseases such as diabetes, cardiovascular disease, and certain cancers— especially colon and breast cancers. Additionally, exercise has been shown to improve mental health, quality of sleep, quality of life, and mood.

EXERCISE AS A KEYSTONE HABIT

Regular exercise is part of living a healthy lifestyle. In addition to its physical benefits such as increased bone density, weight loss, and the prevention of chronic disease, exercise has many benefits to overall health, including mental wellness, skincare, and pain management.

Exercise can also be a "keystone" habit — a habit that has the effect of triggering other positive habits. Exercise can start a chain of good habits: better sleep, better eating, and better personal choices.

"Typically, people who exercise start eating better and becoming more productive at work. They smoke less and show more patience with colleagues and family. They use their credit cards less frequently and say they feel less stressed. Exercise is a keystone habit that triggers widespread change."

— Charles Duhigg

Because there are so many kinds of exercise, there's no need to suffer through something that's just not right for you. You might like the adrenaline from running, the calm from yoga, the strength from weightlifting, or the challenge from CrossFit.

Developing a regular exercise routine that suits your fitness style will increase your energy, improve your mindset, and help make physical activity both enjoyable and sustainable. If you love competition, competitive sports may be your perfect match. On the other hand, if you don't like crowds, you may not feel comfortable in group classes.

Like food, think creatively about exercise. Be curious to try the right combination of exercise that suits you physically, mentally, and emotionally. Find the time of day, duration, and intensity-level that fits your schedule and preferences. When adding exercise into your routine, remember that your body also needs rest and relaxation to maximize the benefits of exercise and to recover. So, give yourself a minimum one day a week for rest.

Listen to your body and learn how to challenge and protect yourself. Your goal is to create a habit of exercising, so find something that can work for you for the long term. Take a moment to reflect on the mental, emotional, and physical hurdles in your way, and see where they can be adjusted for an overall better experience.

EXERCISE AND MENTAL HEALTH

Regular exercise can improve your mental health, including the reduction of depression and anxiety symptoms in adults. Studies have shown that regular, low-intensity exercise, continued over long periods of time, can lead to increased release of neurotrophic proteins, which in turn can lead to better brain function and help relieve depression symptoms in some people. Exercise also improves your cardiovascular system, leading to more energy as your heart and lungs work more efficiently, making you feel more energized.

While it may seem difficult to add exercise to an already busy schedule, keep in mind that any kind of exercise can provide stress relief. Exercise not only releases endorphins, which make you feel better but also can help release tensions that your body may have been holding throughout the day. Exercise can also provide an opportunity for the brain to "turn off," resetting stresses and anxieties build up throughout the day.

EXERCISE AND SKIN HEALTH

Exercise has many benefits for your skin. In addition to the short-term benefits of giving an "instant glow," the increased blood flow and stress-relieving qualities of physical activity can also reduce acne and slow the skin-aging process.

Because exercise increases blood flow and circulation, regular exercise can help mitigate skin problems. Exercise causes pores to dilate, which allows sweat to remove any oils or bacteria that could cause acne. To maximize the benefits of this process, those who suffer from acne should promptly wash acne-prone areas with a gentle cleanser to remove impurities after exercising to prevent breakouts.

Additionally, with careful mitigation of body temperature, hydration, clothing, and oncoming outbreaks, people with skin conditions such as eczema or rosacea can find exercise activities that work for them. Some possibilities include swimming, exercising indoors, taking frequent breaks during workouts to cool down and wearing exercise gear that is light and breathable allowing sweat to easily evaporate off your skin. Look for cotton fabrics that are soft on the skin and looser fitting so they don't irritate skin.

As our skin matures, it replaces cells more slowly and loses elasticity. Studies have shown that participants who exercise more frequently have younger-looking skin. The benefits are not just cumulative — those who started an exercise routine later in adult life still had younger-looking skin after routine exercise.

QUICK TIPS FOR SKIN SAFETY

Protect your skin during exercise.

- Before exercise: use a mineral-based SPF for outdoor exercise year-round and use a hairband or elastic to keep hair out of your eyes and face, to reduce the irritation and create a barrier against sweat.

- During exercise: dress for the season and use layers to manage your body temperature and sweat. Try UV-blocking clothing year-round for easy sun protection. Find lightweight, wicking layers for cooler weather.

- After exercise: A cooling, hydrating mist can replenish the skin after strenuous workouts. This helps the skin return to its normal temperature and can help reduce redness.

FRESH AIR AND NATURE

My family has had a small, summer place in the Adirondacks on middle Saranac, the lower Saranac River and Oseetah Lake for five generations. We still enjoy our time in the woods, hiking on the peaks of the beautiful mountains, kayaking, canoeing, fishing, and swimming in the cool lake water. I always look forward to getting out of the car when we first arrive and taking in a big breath of the pine-scented Adirondack air.

If you look back on your childhood, I am sure you have memories of getting outside: going out on the first snow day, wearing short sleeves on the first warm spring day, swimming outside in the summer, walking in the sweet, crisp fall air. We know the pleasure and calm these moments bring. But for some reason, it feels so hard to make time for disconnecting from technology and connecting with nature.

For many of us, our lifestyle has us spending the majority of our day indoors and centered around computers and our phones. We are working long days and taking very little time off. Children spend more time inside playing digital games or watching movies, rather than running around outside. This is a hectic, and disconnected way to live — and a cause for chronic stress, starting at a very young age. Maybe this is part of the reason 12.7% of our population is on antidepressants, an increase of over 400% since the 1980s according to an analysis from the National Center for Health Statistics.

"An EPA study found that Americans spend approximately 90% of their time indoors... We are, after all, animals, and it's hard to forget that, even if some try really hard, surrounding themselves with walls, metal, glass, and screens. Those people tend to pay a price, often with their health and quality of life."

— NPR

A History of Outdoor Healing

In the mid-to-late 1800s, people traveled to the Adirondacks to breathe cold, fresh air as a treatment for tuberculosis. Dr. Edward Trudeau set up four sanatoriums in Tupper Lake, Saranac Lake, and Ray Brook in the Adirondack Mountains of New York.

With tuberculosis rampant in crowded cities, factories, and tenements, fresh air was thought to be important for patients' recovery, and a considerable body of medical opinion was convinced that the aroma of pine or spruce trees provided therapeutic benefit.

Trudeau reported the benefits of the natural chemicals secreted by evergreen trees, collectively known as "phytoncide," and associated them with improvements in the activity of frontline immune defenders. They have antibacterial and antifungal qualities which help plants fight disease. In Germany, physicians Peter Detweiler and Hermann Brehmer set up sanatoriums in their pine forests with the same results.

John Muir was ahead of his time when he realized the healing powers of nature from daily stress in the 1800s:

"Thousands of tired, nerve-shaken, over-civilized people are beginning to find out that going to the mountains is going home; that wildness is a necessity; and that mountain parks and reservations are useful not only as fountains of timber and irrigating rivers, but as fountains of life.

— John Muir

John Muir's philosophy is very simple: spending time in a natural outdoor environment and walking in a relaxed way has calming, healing, rejuvenating, and restorative benefits. A gentle walk in nature will improve your mood and feelings of happiness, as well as reduce stress.

It is believed that chronic stress and release of cortisol and other stress hormones are the underlying factors in headaches, migraines, weight gain, high blood pressure, heart problems, heart disease, anxiety, diabetes, skin conditions, asthma, arthritis, digestive problems, and memory loss as well as autoimmune conditions and other ailments.

JAPANESE FOREST BATHING

Taking a break, getting a big breath of fresh air, and feeling the warmth of the sun on your skin can have many health benefits. Japanese researchers in the 1980s developed a concept called "Shinrin-yoku," which means "forest bathing" or "taking in the forest atmosphere." It has become a fundamental part of healing many conditions, as well as preventive care.

Understanding the benefits of spending time outdoors in a forest or park seems intuitive. There is no fixed quantity of how much nature a person should enjoy or how much time to spend connecting to the outdoors. Instead, it is a question of internal reflection and defining what works best for you.

Exposure to sunlight and fresh air offers your body health benefits that can last a lifetime. Forest bathing stimulates an increase in the parasympathetic nervous system activity which prompts rest, conserves energy, and slows down the heart rate while increasing intestinal and gland activity, and improving digestion. The reduced adrenal activity lowers cortisol and other stress hormones, calming the body's stress-response system.

This reduction in stress hormones boosts our immune defenses. The body's frontline defenders, such as antiviral natural killer cells, are suppressed by stress hormones. Since forest bathing can lower stress-hormone production and elevate mood states, it's not surprising that it also influences markers of immune-system strength.

According to shinrin-yoku.org, the scientifically proven benefits of Shinrin-yoku include:

- Boosted immune system functioning, with an increase in the count of the body's Natural Killer (NK) cells.

- Reduced blood pressure

- Reduced stress

- Improved mood

- Increased ability to focus, even in children with ADHD

- Accelerated recovery from surgery or illness

- Increased energy level

- Improved sleep

THE SCIENCE BEHIND IT

Harvard Health Publishing reports on some of the health benefits of going outdoors:

- Vitamin D levels increase from sunshine, which may help protect the body from "osteoporosis to cancer to depression to heart attacks and strokes."

- Exercise levels increase, especially for children.

- Exercising in nature (called "green exercise") helps improve mental health, with some studies showing that "just five minutes of green exercise resulted in improvements in self-esteem and mood."

- Concentration improves. Richard Louv coined the term "nature-deficit disorder" in his 2008 *book Last Child in the Woods*. Researchers reported that children with ADHD seem to focus better after being outdoors. A study published in 2008 found that children with ADHD scored higher on a test of concentration after a walk through a park than after a walk through a residential neighborhood or downtown area.

- Patients experience faster healing, less pain, and decreased stress when exposed to nature.

QUICK TIPS FOR FRESH-AIR ROUTINES

Use technology to your benefit. It's hard to carve out time for nature, but it can be planned. Take a look at your calendar, and make some time for daily, weekly, and monthly time in nature. Add them to your calendar so you are sure that all of the other tasks of life don't take over!

- Daily: Take a 10-minute walk.

- Weekly: Make time for a one-hour walk outdoors, with your smartphone off (or on airplane mode) so that you can be undistracted. Try this alone or with friends or family.

- Monthly: Plan a half-day or full-day spent outdoors at local parks and nature preserves. For many people, you can plan an outing that's a short trip away. Wake up early, pack a lunch, and take yourself and your loved ones to explore nature nearby.

RELATIONSHIPS

Relationships are the cornerstone of life. They speak to our ability to love and relate to other human beings. We all need to connect with others and feel the love and support those relationships bring.

Often relationships are tested by the pace and stresses of modern life. Personally, I have experienced great rewards from fostering positive relationships and ending those that are not. Relationships are a critical buffer to your health, providing social value, emotional support, and actual stress reduction. Relationships are work, but they should make you feel good.

"Knowing that we can be loved exactly as we are gives us all the best opportunity for growing into the healthiest of people."

— Fred Rogers

HEALTH AND PERSONAL RELATIONSHIPS

There is a wide spectrum of relationships — from close partners and siblings to clerks and colleagues. Each can have a positive impact on your life, as we build positive and rewarding engagements. Close, personal relationships have shown to have a broad range of positive benefits. Studies have also shown that people in constructive relationships:

- Live longer, due to reduced stress and healthier habits

- Heal more quickly, with social support for recovery

- Feel happier: positive relationships produce more oxytocin — a hormone that promotes feelings of love, bonding, and wellbeing

- Make healthier choices, with a partner for support and accountability

FRIENDSHIPS

Friendships also play a key role in health and happiness. Unfortunately, studies have found that women often drop time with friends as their lives get busier. A recent survey on stress found that of the respondents:

- 51% of the women say that they don't see friends at all in an average week

- 35% of men say they don't see friends at all in an average week

Women actually get a bigger hit of oxytocin than men when around friends, so there are counterintuitive benefits to making time for seeing friends. In a culture where women often prioritize others first, they often don't see friends as much as would be beneficial and healthy. Of course, relationships for men also have great value — providing support, trust, connection, and quality time.

"We don't need proximity and face-to-face interactions all the time, but we do need a daily dose."

— Dr. Stephen W. Porges

TOXIC RELATIONSHIPS

But what about relationships that don't serve our health and wellbeing? Likely you have had to manage, or cut ties with, a relationship that caused you stress, anxiety, or unhappiness. This can be difficult to navigate in the workplace, where you may have little choice in your interactions. This can be doubly difficult with a close friend or family member.

While very complex or entangled relationships may require professional help, you can also look to the following steps to address difficult relationships on your own:

- Define your own truth.

- Try to separate facts from emotional opinions and make clear decisions.

- Express your truth after thoughtful consideration. Your words should pass through three gates: Is it true? Is it kind? Is it necessary?

- Create boundaries for the behaviors you will not accept.

- Take great care of yourself.

- Foster and strengthen relationships with positive friends and family members who support you.

"You can love them, forgive them, want good things for them…but still move on without them."

— Mandy Hale

COMMUNITY

One of my great pleasures is building connections and giving back to my local community. Finding the local community groups — from religious organizations, social clubs, or even group exercise classes — can connect you to a world of people with shared interests and values.

RELATIONSHIP RITUALS

How do you build a social life that fosters positive relationships? Making room for rituals of relationship-building can help your overall health and happiness. Here are some starting suggestions:

- Daily phone call check-ins.

- Texting check-ins with remote friends.

- A shared weekly activity, like a class, a walk, or even a TV show, that you do with a friend or family member.

- Monthly activities with a group of friends, from potlucks to dinner parties, sports events, happy hours, yoga or workouts, connecting outdoors for a hike, or even a book club.

WORK

Work can be a great source of accomplishment, connection, and reward. Whether it is paid work for a company, running your own business, or unpaid caretaking, finding the work that brings you satisfaction is incredibly valuable to your health and wellbeing.

On the flip side, stressful work can cause great harm. Short-term stress or overworking can lead to skipping meals and exercise and losing sleep. Longer-term job stress has also been linked to hypertension, obesity, and poor mental health.

For most of us, we must work. Finding a vocation that you love and enjoy on a day-to-day basis is an important task. Having a generally positive experience can help you ride through the difficulties and challenges that are also, unfortunately, a part of work life.

FINDING YOUR WORK PASSION

If I could tell you the job that would make you happiest, well, I would probably stop writing this book and move in a new professional direction. There is no perfect recipe I've found for finding work that you are passionate about, but I do believe that the right job has a combination of the following:

- People you enjoy and trust

- An overall goal that aligns with your values

- Fair compensation

- Some control over the work you do

- Day-to-day tasks that you generally like doing (with the minority of your time spent doing tasks you don't enjoy)

YOUR BEST JOB

Determining your best job is a personal endeavor. Your best job may be as an accountant, where your best friend's worst nightmare could be to work as an accountant. Looking at the criteria above, you can start thinking about the type of organization and day-to-day tasks that will make a job satisfying, rewarding, and healthy.

Your best job may mean different things for you at different points of life.

- If you are risk-averse and ambitious, your best job may be one where you can move up the ladder at a well-established company.

- If you are entrepreneurial and driven, your best job may be one where you can run your own business.

- If you are focused on gaining material wealth, your best job may be the highest paid one you can achieve, with the opportunity to earn more over time.

- If you are balancing caretaking, education, hobbies, or other activities, your best job may be one that offers flexibility.

- If you enjoy traveling or have a partner who must travel, your best job may be one that allows remote work.

"Remember that work and life coexist. Wellness at work follows you home and vice-versa. The same goes for when you're not well fueled or fulfilled. Work and life aren't opposing forces to balance; they go hand-in-hand and are intertwined as different elements of the same person: you."

— Melissa Steginus

OUR NEW SECOND JOB: SMARTPHONE MANAGER

The work landscape has changed drastically in the past 50 years. When Don Draper left the office, he maybe took a briefcase with him, but his phone and job remained in the office.

Now with smartphones, our jobs can follow us anywhere. While it's easy to scroll through email during a quiet moment, for our health and happiness, it's worth setting boundaries for getting "off the clock."

Fundamentally, we must practice mindful phone usage. As anyone who's tried knows, it's harder than you would think. But know this: you can be more productive if you have a limited time to do focused work.

Reading emails multiple times (at night before you go to bed, in the morning when you wake up, again when you sit at your desk) wastes your time and brainpower, making your workstyle less efficient.

Be mindful of when you are "working" (even if it is multitasking with other activities) and "not working." If you are responding to emails while preparing dinner, ask yourself how this is compromising the quality of both efforts.

You probably don't need to participate in a culture of instant, shallow responses. What if you waited until you had a dedicated block of time to respond thoughtfully?

Here are a few tips to help you set borders around your off-work hours:

- Set your calendar to show the hours you are not in the office.

- Make a policy of not answering emails and only emergency phone calls for certain periods of time.

- Add a note in your email signature that you don't check emails after 5 pm (or whatever is right for you) or on weekends.

For managers looking to foster an environment where "around the clock" is not the expectation, you can:

- Define the key method of communication and use during work hours. Maybe it's email, Slack, Messenger, or text message. Having clear work-designated spaces during work-designated times helps manage the communications flow.

- If you are working off-hours, schedule emails or messages to send in the morning (rather than sending immediately).

- Set an expectation. For example: "Unless it's marked urgent, I don't expect you to answer emails after 5 pm the same day."

Technology also offers one of the perks of working now. Laptops, cell phones, and portable Wi-Fi mean you can work from many more places than you could ever before. This can be a great thing for ambitious workers looking to learn and do more when they are out of the office, workers wanting to work remotely, and workers looking for flexible schedules.

MAKING LEMONADE OUT OF LEMONS

If you have a job that generally aligns with your values, your personality, and your situation, you are likely willing to take on tasks you don't enjoy, because the good outweighs the bad. We all have tasks we don't enjoy - filing expense reports, vacuuming under the couch, and filling out paperwork, to name a few. But what if the bad starts outweighing the good? Some jobs, like toxic relationships, you might just need to quit.

But if your job has the potential to improve, consider looking at the following opportunities:

- Reaching out to managers and peers and other people in the organization who you can get to know.

- Understanding the company's goals and playing a part in moving the company forward.

- Negotiating compensation you want by understanding the market, your value, and your industry.

- Finding opportunities to own your projects or be a part of bigger projects.

- Assessing whether you are doing more tasks you dislike than tasks you like, and see where you can change the balance: with different tools, different distribution of work, a different job, or a different approach to solving the problem.

DOING YOUR BEST WORK

Earlier, we talked about finding your best job. There's also another component: doing your best work. Your work life doesn't have to be separate from the rest of your life and bringing intention, care, and compassion can make your work higher quality and personally more fulfilling.

That can mean everything from bringing your best self to your work environment, taking pride in the tasks that you do, and practicing kindness and fairness with coworkers. There's no escaping difficult days and difficult times, but I find that there is a deep satisfaction in trying my best.

BALANCING WORK AND LIFE

As I wrote at the beginning of this chapter, there are numerous health benefits to finding a happy balance between work and life. First, finding a job that gives you pleasure and is your best job (however you define it) can help your overall happiness and sense of purpose. Second, managing your job stress can help prevent stress-related physical and mental health issues.

Not only that, but striking a balance between working and non-working can make you more productive at work and happier in your off time. To help create a balance, consider the following:

- Foster positive relationships in your workplace.

- Find joy in your day-to-day work tasks, even attaching a sense of accomplishment to the tasks you don't love doing.

- Use meditation, exercise, or time with friends to manage work stress you may feel during off-work hours.

- Disconnect from your job obligations for set hours each day.

- While at home, make time for "not working" each day.

- Get restful sleep.

THE BEAUTY OF DE-STRESSING

"Stress" is a general term for the feeling that our responsibilities have exceeded our capacity for coping. It leads to an overall feeling of "too much." Our worlds are full of potential stressors, but too much stress on your body can affect your total wellbeing.

Stress is anything that presents a challenge or a threat to our wellbeing. While it originally functioned to protect humans from natural predators, today's stressors are caused less by tiger attacks and more by day-to-day aggravators such as traffic, work, or family responsibilities.

However, today's human bodies still respond with the same instincts our ancestors did. Physiologically, when the body feels threatened, an "alarm system" triggers your hormones to redistribute bodily functions deemed non-essential to immediate survival.

Stress comes from a wide range of sources and manifests itself differently in different bodies. Stress can be caused by juggling family commitments; trying to stay on top of work; maintaining relationships; uncertainty; large changes in lifestyle, such as marriage or death of a relative; or external and environmental factors, to name a few.

The way that the body responds to stress varies from person to person as well, but there are some common trends.

- Have you noticed a dull, lingering ache in your neck or your head?

- Are your shoulders or jaw often clenched?

- Do you eat more or less than usual?

- Are you seeing facial lines and wrinkles deepen?

- Do you suffer from occasional indigestion?

- How well do you sleep, and for how long?

While they may seem unrelated, these issues can all be effects of stress.

THE FIGHT OR FLIGHT RESPONSE

Directly related to the physiological responses of stress, is the body's immediate "fight or flight" response controlled by our sympathetic nervous system. When faced with a challenge or a threat, your body activates resources to protect you — either to get away as fast as you can or to fight.

The experience of stress releases "stress hormones" that aid the body and the mind in coping quickly with the stressful situation. The "fight or flight" reflex is the mental response to stressors. It is called the sympathetic nervous system. When it is triggered, your body produces larger quantities of the chemicals cortisol, adrenaline, and noradrenaline, which then trigger a higher heart rate, heightened muscle preparedness, sweating, and alertness. All these factors help us protect ourselves in a dangerous or challenging situation.

The liver also fuels that reaction with a surge of glucose, the body's gasoline. This whole-body response causes the heart to race, muscles to tense, blood pressure to rise, stomach acid to increase, and attention to sharpen all at once.

Non-essential body functions slow down, such as our digestive and immune systems when we are in "fight or flight" response mode. All resources can then be concentrated on rapid breathing, blood flow, alertness, and muscle use. If the stress dissipates, then hormone, glucose, and blood pressure levels usually go back to normal.

While humans are no longer often fighting for their immediate survival, these "fight or flight" instincts can be triggered by everyday modern stressors. While the response is natural, reducing stress where possible is key to improving your life and reducing the risks that long-term stress poses on the body and mind.

While "fight or flight" is the sympathetic nervous system, "rest and digest" is the parasympathetic nervous system. The parasympathetic nervous system slows down body functions and relaxes the body.

When our sympathetic nervous system can relax and the parasympathetic nervous system becomes more active, healing, repair, and rejuvenation take place and other bodily functions are optimized, helping us to look and feel our best.

EFFECTS OF STRESS

Stress is not a new phenomenon. Hippocrates stated all diseases stem from an imbalance in the body, such as stress. Archaeologists have found physiological evidence of stress on skeletons from medieval London.

In 1983, *Time Magazine* ran a cover story titled "Stress: Can We Cope?" Recent studies have shown that stress and related complaints and ailments are responsible for 75 to 90% of all doctor visits. Stress is so common that the National Institute of Occupational Safety and Health has declared stress a hazard of the workplace.

"Rule Number One is, don't sweat the small stuff. Rule Number Two is, it's all small stuff. And if you can't fight and you can't flee, flow."

— University of Nebraska cardiologist Robert Eliot

Stress has many effects on the body, both physically and mentally. When stressed, the body prepares itself by ensuring that enough sugar or energy is readily available. While this can provide a boost of energy in the short term, prolonged stress makes the adrenal glands and heart work overtime and a body under constant stress may not properly metabolize the extra blood sugar.

Chronic stress can cause the body to produce more stomach acid, leading to stress-triggered indigestion, heartburn, or acid reflux, in addition to stomachache, vomiting, and other gastrointestinal discomforts. Over time, this can lead to weight gain, diabetes, and digestive or other metabolic issues, as well as stroke, heart attack, and hypertension.

Because it triggers a change in blood pressure and hormone levels in the body, stress can have a wide range of physical impacts on the body. This includes body aches and pains, or headaches from tensing muscles without allowing them to relax. The increased heart rate can affect breathing, which can trigger asthma or emphysema.

By overtaxing the immune system, the body can become more susceptible to ailments such as colds and the flu. Libido can also seriously suffer from the effects of stress, as it is so closely related to blood pressure, hormones, and mental focus. Additionally, studies have shown that increased stress can lead to worsened outbreaks of acne vulgaris.

Stress can also impact mental health. Possible consequences of stress include increased anxiety, anger, and depression, and decreased motivation and sleep quality. Stress can lead to feelings of being overwhelmed, easily irritated, or generally upset and unhappy. It can trigger more unhealthy behaviors such as overconsumption of harmful foods and substances like tobacco and alcohol, undereating, or a decrease in social energy. Overall, stress can greatly impact quality of life, physically and mentally, if not successfully balanced.

"If you don't think your anxiety, depression, sadness, and stress impact your physical health, think again. All of these emotions trigger chemical reactions in your body, which can lead to inflammation and a weakened immune system. Learn how to cope, sweet friend. There will always be dark days."

– Kris Carr

The body systems are interconnected, so stress is not "confined" to one place or one bodily response. Different people will have different physical and mental responses to stress triggers, sometimes manifesting across different parts of the body. For example, people who work at computers all day can have neck and back pain, caused by sitting for prolonged stretches with bad posture, giving muscles no time to fully relax, and "locking" into misalignment.

Work stress and bad posture can affect facial skin. Sleep deprivation from stress can then worsen muscular pain. Over a short time, the combination of pain and lack of sleep can cause facial muscles to tense up and accentuate the appearance of wrinkles from environmental damage. Additionally, the change in hormone levels in the body can slow down the natural recovery processes, causing the face to "age" more quickly.

While some stress is inevitable, there are ways to mitigate the effects of stress on the body and mind.

DIGITAL DETOX

Digital detox is a recent term used to describe choosing to disconnect for some time. This can range from smartphones to laptops, to gaming devices, and television. Doing a digital detox and reducing media inputs for a period of time can help reduce stress levels.

How often do you feel "on the hook" to respond to texts, check on social media, scan your email, or switch on the news? Fear of missing out is a real thing, and many of us feel it when we misplace our phones or the internet/cable goes out.

A study from the American Psychological Association found that about 18% of adults in the U.S. find that technology is a significant source of stress in their lives. Short periods of disconnecting can help reduce the noise, giving you the quiet and time to reconnect with your thoughts and relax your mind. It's also a practice: as you become more comfortable with not being constantly connected, you can increase the breaks you take from your digital life.

"So attached are we to our devices that it's not unusual to have your phone with you at all times. We carry our phones around everywhere as if they are epi-pens and we all have fatal allergies."

– Charlotte Lieberman

SLEEP, RELAXATION, AND RESTORATION

The importance of a good night's sleep now has to compete with the demands of our hectic, non-stop schedules. We've grown to be a society that relies on stimulants to keep us going and energize us to keep up with the demands of the day, and relaxants to then help us calm down to sleep.

Lifestyles can be full without running ourselves into the ground. The truth is that we need to get enough sleep and rest to rejuvenate, to allow our body to heal from the stressors of the day, and to function properly and more successfully. Burnout is a symptom of our non-stop pace of life.

Many stimulants constantly bombard us in a variety of forms — light, sound, movement, and information — that disrupt our bodies' natural circadian rhythms. Our ability to achieve restorative, quality sleep is compromised and we are left feeling exhausted and drained. This creates a vicious cycle which may lead us to gain weight, lose mental clarity, feel emotionally drained, and eventually have our general health diminished.

"Take plenty of exercise. Always be cheerful. Take all the sleep you need. You may expect to be well."

— James Freeman Clarke

As the day comes to a close, you can try a few of these things to encourage a good night's sleep and improve how you look and feel.

ALIGN WITH NATURE

The average adult should strive for six to eight hours of sleep nightly after the age of 18. Work to be closer to nature. When the sun goes down, we should sleep. When the sun rises, we rise. Nature provides perfect harmony. We should strive to get to bed as early as we can, in an effort to enjoy the recommended six to eight hours of sleep.

GET EXERCISE

Getting 30 minutes of moderate aerobic exercise daily can help improve sleep quality, and research suggests that exercise can reduce the effects of insomnia. Exercise can help you fall asleep more quickly and improve the quality of slow wave or deep sleep. However, be careful not to exercise too close to bedtime.

REDUCE BLUE LIGHT EXPOSURE

The blue light that is emitted from computer screens, smartphones, tablets, streetlights, light bulbs, and even LED lights affects our brain's ability to produce melatonin, a hormone that tells your body when it's time to go to sleep. Blue light wakes you up and tells your brain that it's daytime, keeping you from having a good night's sleep.

Here are the best ways to protect yourself from too much blue light exposure:

- Get off electronics at least two hours before bed. That includes scanning social media platforms and answering emails.
- Charge your phone and keep unnecessary electronics outside of the bedroom.

- Never have a television in your bedroom or use it to fall asleep.

- Have room darkening shades or curtains on your bedroom windows.

LIGHT FOOD, SOOTHING DRINKS

To sleep more restfully, avoid eating heavy meals before bed as they keep your digestive system working. Try taking a small dose of melatonin (the hormone responsible for sleepiness) with a cup of soothing herbal tea or a glass of tart cherry juice which is naturally melatonin-rich two hours before bed to help encourage a good night's sleep.

MEDITATION

Meditation before bed is an excellent way to quiet your mind and your thoughts. Science shows that meditation significantly lowers stress and reduces anxiety. It has been proven to rewire your brain, strengthening neural pathways that calm your nervous system. Even five minutes per day can have amazing health benefits, including increasing your ability to have a peaceful night's sleep.

"During the time of stress, the "fight-or-flight" response is on and the self-repair mechanism is disabled. It is then when we say that the immunity of the body goes down and the body is exposed to the risk for disease. Meditation activates relaxation when the sympathetic nervous system is turned off and the parasympathetic nervous system is turned on, and natural healing starts."

— Annie Wilson, Effect of Meditation on Cardiovascular Health, Immunity & Brain Fitness

DEEP RELAXATION AND THE ROLE OF REGULAR SPA VISITS

There are numerous reasons people visit a spa, but the most significant is to combat the effects stress has on the body. Relaxation is important because it helps us reduce the effects of stress, and spas are developed to provide a stress-free space.

The human body is designed to experience both positive and negative stress, keeping us alert and ready to act. Stress only becomes negative when we have continuous challenges without any real relief. This leads to increased tension and a perpetual feeling that the body is under attack. Your spa experience helps to release those negative stress hormones.

For this reason, spas recommend a prolonged stay, before and after one's appointment, rather than rushing out as soon as the treatment is finished. By enjoying your spa experience before and after your treatment, you are allowing your mind and body to calm the sympathetic nervous system, release its tension, and heal.

This relaxation is a very important part of the entire experience and compounds the benefits you will take away. The time surrounding the service should be as good for you as the results from the service itself.

A spa visit can jumpstart a healthy lifestyle, whether you are concerned with aching joints and sore muscles, weight loss, or a chronic skin condition. It offers the relief needed from the negative stress that surrounds us daily.

The spa is a place to remove our bodies from the hectic lifestyle to which we have grown accustomed, and to relieve stress, fatigue, and other consequences of constantly rushing. A spa visit can help rejuvenate and re-energize the body, clear the mind, and help improve rest and relaxation.

Spas are designed to encourage relaxation. From quiet music to comfortable robes and heated tables, the goal is to design a space that is inviting and serene. Spa therapists and team members are trained professionals who are there to work with your individual needs.

Spa therapists should be attentive to your personal needs and relaxation goals, completing a consultation before starting any treatments, identifying problems, and keeping you informed throughout your treatment. Afterward, you should take additional time to "ramp up" again slowly before continuing about your day.

After a spa treatment, the therapist should take some time to educate you on any conditions they found during the treatment and recommend what products to use at home to maintain the results and also suggest an appropriate timeline to return for continued care.

While a single spa visit is beneficial, routine care and a complete wellness program will produce the best long-term results to have you looking and feeling your best. A successful spa program is a partnership between you and your spa professional, and it is greatly impacted by how well you take care of yourself between visits.

Regular spa visits can help reverse or prevent many physical side effects of stress and improve overall health through relaxation. Committing to this will help get the most out of your spa experience.

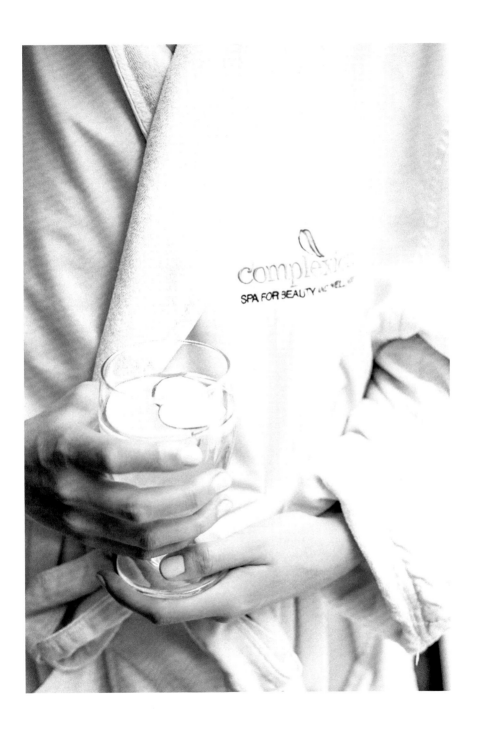

CREATE YOUR AT-HOME SPA

For the times in between visits, you can recreate the spa experience by making your home a place of calm and relaxation. Even if you have a small space, simple choices can change the atmosphere in your home.

- Change into comfortable clothing: find soft, breathable, and comfortable clothes that you can slip into after a day of being dressed for work (whether heels, scrubs, suits, or jeans).

- Find a quiet corner that can be a space for reading, journaling, or meditating. Clear it from clutter and make it a place you can go to easily. Keep it separate from your phone, computer, or other technology.

- Selects scents that relax you, and find candles, essential oils, and diffusers that you can easily use in your home.

- Stay hydrated. Love the fruit water or herbal teas at the spa? Keep a water pitcher infused with fresh fruit, cucumber, and mint in your fridge. Make a large thermos full of herbal tea and keep it on your counter for easy access.

- Create a playlist of music that calms and relaxes you. Many streaming music services have pre-programmed playlists that you can browse and customize.

De-Stressing Scents:

- Lavender
- Ylang ylang
- Lemon
- Bergamot
- Chamomile
- Jasmine
- Holy basil
- Sweet basil
- Rose
- Vetiver
- Geranium

De-Stressing Herbs for Tea:

- Chamomile
- Peppermint
- Rose
- Lemon Balm
- Fennel
- Ginseng
- Dandelion

SELF-CARE

Self-care is often thought of as an occasional indulgence; a single visit to the spa or salon or taking a moment to soak in a luxurious bath at home wearing a facial mask. It can be seen as something that we occasionally allow ourselves to enjoy. This mindset does not serve us, because it does not acknowledge the vital importance of self-care.

In this modern world, it takes a lot of effort to create space in which we care for ourselves. There are, however, huge health benefits. Keeping a balance of nutritious eating and exercise can help improve immunity and resistance to stress. Spending time in the outdoors has proven to have de-stressing benefits. Time for happy, healthy relationships and balancing work and life has shown to have measurable impacts on health.

Self-care embodies the lifestyle we are talking about in this very book. It is a decision to do the things that are good for us and to do them regularly. Activities that nurture and refuel us at a deep level can help foster a stronger sense of self, happiness, and wellbeing.

LIVING INTENTIONALLY AND JOURNALING

In a busy, fast-paced world, taking a moment and making decisions with intention is a method for making sure your choices are based on your values and goals.

There are many benefits to slowing down and truly assessing whether your day-to-day choices are helping live the life you want. It also may be difficult to untangle your personal desires from social expectations, cultural norms, or comparisons to other people. In a culture that values material goods, where social media allows for instant comparison, and expectations may not align with your personal happiness, it is worth the time to make sure you are living according to your own values.

Living intentionally is made up of a few steps:

1. See the choices: understand that your life is made up of choices that you can control.
2. Decide the values: choose the values you want to live by. These values can come from religious or spiritual beliefs, health practices, personal growth, or social mores.
3. Define your purpose: what is your reason for being, and for being with others?
4. Set goals: think about and write down the goals that align with your values.
5. Stay focused: remove distractions from your goals. This might include having device-free time, limiting time on social media, or limiting time spent in unhealthy relationships.
6. Keep curious: keep learning and growing from the people and ideas around you. Seek out books, resources, lectures, and events that help foster your growth and development.

"How we spend our days is, of course, how we spend our lives."

— Annie Dillard

WRITING EXERCISE: MORNING PAGES

Morning pages is a concept created by Julia Cameron, author of *The Artist's Way*. Designed especially for creative work, it is also a challenging and inspiring method of journaling. The idea is to write a few pages in the first minutes you wake up, and that capturing these unfiltered thoughts allows you to access your innermost introspection and dreams. To get started, keep a journal next to your bed. In the first moments that you are awake, write:

- Memories of any dreams you have had

- Ten things from the previous day that you are grateful for

- Then write in a stream of consciousness without self-censorship, just a page or two

This is a type of intention-setting and meditation. Try it and see how it feels.

MINDFUL MEDITATION

Meditation, the processes of focusing one's mind, has been in practice since 5,000 BC. First developed in India, meditation was created for spiritual purposes. While many still use meditation as part of a religious or spiritual practice, many others have turned to meditation as a tool for relaxation and de-stressing.

Meditation has been shown to have emotional benefits that extend beyond the individual session, including:

- Increased sense of calm
- Stronger sense of perspective on stressful situations
- Reducing negative emotions
- Increased patience

Initial studies have also shown benefits of meditation for managing medical conditions, including:

- Anxiety
- Chronic pain
- Tension headaches
- Sleep issues
- Depression

You can get started with a simple practice of mindful breathing: closing your eyes and counting your breaths in and breaths out. Try it and see what you notice and how you feel. If you are interested in doing more, apps like Calm, Breathe: Meditation, and Headspace make it easy to create a small ritual around de-stressing.

All three apps let you pick from a number of different meditations and goals (for example: meditations for calm, parenting, or focus). A simple practice of mindful breathing — closing your eyes and counting your breaths in and breaths out — can take you out of the stream of daily stresses and re-center your mind. Meditation becomes even more effective by doing just five minutes a day rather than practicing for one hour, once a week.

Some yoga classes also offer meditation as part of the session, while some yoga studios offer dedicated meditation classes. The Chinese practice of qigong combines movement, meditation, and breathing exercises.

Personally, I like to start my morning with a ten-minute meditation that gets me focused on tasks for the day and then end my evening with another five minutes to quiet my mind and help me get a good night's sleep. There are definitely some days that this is harder to do than others, but as a general rule this is something I gain a lot of benefit from when I am consistent. It's part of my self-care regimen and I try my best to make it routine.

SKINCARE

Your skin is the largest organ in your body and performs many important functions. It is an active, living tissue that acts as a protective armor to shield us against harmful microbes, UV lights, and infection. It also protects us against harmful textures and temperatures. It is the main barrier between you and the outside world. Beyond esthetics, the skin is key in biofactory and metabolic processes of the body.

As a practicing esthetician and spa owner, I know first-hand the benefits and pleasure of building a regimen that takes care of your skin and body's appearance along with your health. We've talked about nutrition and mental health. Here, I'll go into the science of our skin so you, too, can understand how this organ works and how you can nurture and care for it as well.

There are three main layers of the skin: the epidermis, dermis, and hypodermis, also known as the subcutaneous tissue. Each layer has its own independent features and benefits.

"I'm a big believer in that if you focus on good skincare, you really won't need a lot of makeup."

– Demi Moore

EPIDERMIS

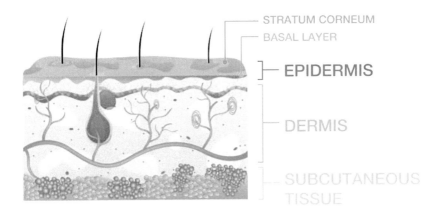

The epidermis is also known as the scarf-skin, the outermost layer of skin that is visible and works to provide protection for the body. This is also where we feel the sensation of touch. There are no blood vessels in this layer and it relies on the underlying layers for nutrients.

The epidermis mainly consists of cells called keratinocytes, which make up keratin, a tough protein found in hair and nails. There are four types of skin cells; keratinocytes, melanocytes, Merkel cells, and Langerhans cells, that are formed in the bottom layer of the epidermis known as the basal layer. From here they migrate to the surface.

Once cells reach the surface, they are shed and then replaced by new cells that are moving up. As we age, this migration process slows down, resulting in the surface condition becoming dry and dull, and can have a rough, uneven tone and texture.

The basal layer of the epidermis, where melanocytes are found, is responsible for producing melanin which determines our skin color. Melanin protects us from harmful ultraviolet radiation from sunlight that damages the DNA of skin cells, accelerating aging and at times even causing cancer.

The epidermis is also home to the Langerhans cells. As part of the immune system, these cells detect foreign bodies and infections and are also responsible for allergic reactions. The epidermis is relatively waterproof and prevents the entry of bacteria, viruses, and other harmful foreign substances into the body. It provides protection, which helps keep us healthy on the inside.

Merkel cells are found in the basal layer of the epidermis and are associated with sensory nerve endings which act as receptors for touch and can feel light sensations.

The thickness of the epidermis depends on the wear and tear on that particular part of the body, such as the hands and the soles of the feet. The epidermis is thicker on the soles of the feet and the hands and is thinner on the eyelids. Your hereditary makeup can also dictate how thick the epidermis is. For example, people with darker complexions tend to have a thicker epidermis, giving them greater protection from the sun.

DERMIS

The second layer of the skin, just below the epidermis, is known as the dermis. The epidermal dermal junction joins these two layers. The dermis contains blood vessels which supply the epidermis with nutrients, and it also helps to dispose of and remove waste.

The dermis consists of fibrous, dense dermal connective tissue, made up of collagen and elastin weaved throughout. It serves as a protective cushion for the body, keeping it flexible and supple. Elasticity refers to how well your skin springs back into shape after being pinched or pulled in compression.

The dermis is also home to the sebaceous glands, our hair follicles, and sweat glands, nerve endings, and the lymphatic system. The sebaceous glands secrete oil (otherwise known as sebum) which forms a protective barrier on the skin surface known as the acid mantle. The acid mantle is slightly acidic (4.5-5.5) and is the skin's first line of defense against harmful invaders, bacteria, and viruses. The acid mantle is antibacterial and that helps keep it hydrated.

The sweat glands, or the eccrine glands, regulate body temperature while the nerve endings in the dermal layer sense stimuli such as pressure, pain, temperature, and sends a nerve impulse message to the brain causing a reaction to pull away and avoid danger.

SUBCUTANEOUS TISSUE

The third layer is the subcutaneous tissue. This is the innermost layer of the skin and is made up of adipose tissue or a fatty layer. It provides insulation to help maintain our body temperature, and it also serves as an anchor between the skin and the muscles and underlying organs below the surface. It provides cushion and plumpness to the contours of our face. As we age, we lose this fatty cushion as it thins out and our skin's appearance becomes more chiseled and less plump.

In summary, the skin is the largest organ of the body that has three main functions: protection, regulation, and sensation. It helps to keep us healthy which can impact our overall wellbeing.

I think it's important for consumers to understand the basic functions of the skin so that they're able to make educated decisions when an esthetician, skin professional, or cosmetic salesperson makes recommendations. They are then able to understand the "why" behind suggested products or treatments. It truly is a joint effort: it is a combination of proper home care and professional treatments that keep the skin looking and feeling its best. In this next chapter, we'll discuss more about professional skin treatments.

FACE MAPPING

Face mapping, also known as skin mapping, is an ancient 3000-year-old belief based on Traditional Chinese Medicine and Ayurveda, which is one of the oldest holistic healing systems. In the practice of face mapping, a person's skin is viewed as a reflection of their inner health. It is believed that various areas of your face, or "zones," are connected to specific organs and that skin conditions reveal internal imbalances. These imbalances can show as blemishes, rashes, redness, dryness, or changes in skin color and can be related to hormones, environmental influences, nutrition, and genetics. With face mapping, the area of the face where blemishes are located is thought to be linked to certain internal organs. It guides you to look beyond the surface and to treat the underlying cause of the skin condition.

FOREHEAD

The forehead is thought to be linked to the small intestines and the bladder. Blemishes here could be a result of poor food choices, including processed foods, high fat, too much sugar, and excess alcohol. Sleep deficiency and stress can also be an influence, which makes sense because stress does slow digestion and interrupt sleep, while alcohol and sugar also lead to slow digestion.

To help flush out toxins and aid digestion, swap caffeinated and overly processed drinks with a nice glass of water. Also getting a good night's sleep of at least seven hours a night.

EYEBROWS

The area between the eyebrows corresponds with the liver, which is important to detoxification in the body. Things that can affect toxicity include alcohol, excessive meat, and dairy consumption, and not enough fluids. The stomach has to work overtime to digest these harsh ingredients and this can lead to inflammation in the body. Some experts recommend reducing dairy, red meat, and fast food consumption and eating more leafy vegetables to improve this area of your skin.

EYES

Under the eyes is linked to the kidneys, adrenals, and all fluids within the body. If you're dehydrated, you'll see signs of this as dark circles and puffiness that comes and goes. Try drinking more pure, filtered water and less soda, sugary juices, coffee and caffeinated beverages, and alcohol. Poor circulation and smoking can also be a trigger.

NOSE

The nose corresponds with the heart. Each side of the nose signifies the same side of the heart, and skin issues here might suggest heart-related blockages. Redness, blackheads, oiliness, and breakouts are potentially a sign of blood pressure or cholesterol problems. Poor circulation, gases, and even stomach bloating can be some of the reasons that this facial area may appear inflamed. Improve your heart health by lowering your cholesterol and consuming less salt and sodium-based products. You might also want to up your intake of omega-3 fatty acids, so buy more nuts, fish, and flaxseed.

TEMPLES

The temples represent the kidneys and bladder. Infections or inflammation in these areas can present themselves as acne. Excess sugar, not enough fluids, and medications that aren't agreeing with your body can also show up and have an effect here.

CHEEKS

The cheeks are related to the stomach, spleen, and respiratory system. Poor respiratory health is a common cause of cheek acne. Red cheeks may be a sign of stomach inflammation from stress or poor diet.

Breakouts in the upper cheeks may be linked to smoking or people suffering from allergies, sinus issues, and asthma, or even pollution from urban living. Smokers often have broken and dilated capillaries due to constricting blood flow and less oxygen in the blood.

Another major culprit could be a dirty cell phone screen. Wipe down your phone every night. Avoid caffeine, fatty foods, and alcohol. Stop smoking. Fresh air will do wonders for your lungs, so try to make a habit out of forest bathing and morning walks.

CHIN

The jawline and chin correspond with the hormonal and reproductive system. Jawline breakouts usually happen around the time of your period or in the middle of your cycle. Typically, just before the start of a woman's cycle, there is more progesterone in the skin causing water retention, which results in the skin appearing puffier.

When this occurs, it puts pressure on the pores and creates a narrower pore lining, constricting normal oil flow. Additionally, an increase in testosterone results in sticky and thicker sebum (or oil), causing more congestion during this time of hormonal shift.

Stress can also impact your hormones and have similar effects; therefore, it is very important to take time to destress and ease tension.

The one thing I found consistent in my research about Chinese face mapping as a way to verify what is going on inside the body; is that any part of the face—whether you are focused on the eyes, the cheeks, or the chin—will benefit from eating a diet of whole, fresh foods.

Reducing excessive sugar, fats, alcohol, and caffeine will also help, as will drinking plenty of water. Do the best you can to get outside and connect with nature. Reduce stress in your life through meditation, yoga, and surrounding yourself with people who bring you joy.

All of this will help bring balance to the skin. After all, your skin is a map to what is taking place inside your body.

SKIN DISORDERS

ACNE

Acne is one of the most common skin disorders in the United States, affecting as many as 50 million Americans annually. It typically affects adolescents during puberty due to hormones, but it can occur at any age.

Sebum (oil) is produced by the sebaceous glands in both males and females and is controlled by the sex hormones (androgens). The most active androgen is testosterone which is produced by the ovaries in females, and the testis in males as well as by the adrenal gland.

Stress can impact the production of oil due to the adrenal and therefore can lead to an acne condition. Acne occurs when pores become clogged with excess oil, dead cells, and bacteria that gets congested in the follicles. Acne can appear on the face, back, shoulders, and chest as inflamed red papules, pimples, pustules, blackheads, and whiteheads.

ACNE VULGARIS

There are varying degrees of acne. "Acne Vulgaris" is the medical term for common acne and is considered the

mildest form of acne. It consists of comedones, papules, pustules, nodules, and cysts.

Comedones

A comedo, or basic acne lesion, forms when a follicle becomes clogged with oil and dead cells. Comedones (the plural of comedo) can develop into bumps called whiteheads and blackheads.

- When the tip of the congestion is exposed to air, it oxidizes and turns dark. That is known as a blackhead.
- Whiteheads are comedones that at the surface of the skin are not exposed to the air and stay closed at the tip. They are usually treated the same way as blackheads.

Both are a combination of dead cells, oil, and debris congested and trapped in the follicle. If left unattended, they will block the flow of oil onto the surface of the skin, creating the acid mantle leading to larger pore size and papules. Some skincare products and makeup can contribute to the cause of comedo formation.

Papules

Papules are comedones that become inflamed and irritated. They form a raised bump with redness on the skin. Papules should not be squeezed or picked because that can actually make them worse, pushing them inward instead of out, which can lead to scarring. A large number of papules can indicate a more moderate to severe acne.

Pustules

Pustules are papules that become filled with white or yellow pus and have a red ring at the base. Inflamed papules and pimples can lead to post-inflammatory hyperpigmentation (PIH) and acne scarring.

Nodules

Nodules are solid, elevated areas of tissue or fluid inside or under the skin surface. Nodules are normally benign and often painless bumps that are hard to the touch. They can be very deep and sometimes sensitive to touch. These may be best treated by a medical professional.

Cysts

Cysts are large sebaceous matter filled lesions that are red and look like a boil. They can become infected; however, a vast majority of them do not. They can be painful, like nodules, and both conditions are considered the most severe type of acne.

Acne is considered mild if you have fewer than twenty whiteheads or blackheads and fewer than fifteen pustules or papules. It usually takes about four-to-six weeks to show improvement. More than twenty whiteheads and blackheads and up to fifty inflamed papules and pustules are considered moderate acne, which can take a bit longer to show improvement.

SEVERE CYSTIC ACNE

Severe cystic acne consists of multiple inflamed cysts, nodules, blackheads, and whiteheads. They can be very deep red or even, in some cases, purple. This type of acne is considered to be very severe and can cause scarring. Reducing inflammation is one of the priorities when treating this type of acne.

CAUSES OF ACNE

Keeping in mind that the skin is the largest organ of the body and it reflects what is happening internally, Acne is a symptom that we need to look more closely into. The causes of acne are not only excessive oil production and congestion; the causes can be hormonal changes (like during adolescence or pregnancy) and times of excess stress (as stress affects our hormones, causing us to produce an unbalanced level of androgens). This can result in stickier sebum and more congestion and breakouts.

Polycystic ovarian syndrome. stomach and digestion problems, unhealthy gut, and diet can also potentially lead to an acne condition.

In fact, many skin problems, from acne to eczema, are likely a result of an unbalanced microbiome due to modern life. It is important to not only treat the surface acne condition but also to be mindful of the root cause of the acne. Diet and nutrition along with stress and lifestyle are especially important things to consider and often overlooked. Gut-healthy and anti-inflammatory foods can have a critical impact on your skin's health and appearance. There should be a holistic approach that includes proper professional skincare treatments, clean products for home use, proper diet, and consideration of lifestyle, including reducing stress.

TREATING ACNE

To treat acne, I recommend starting with a professional consultation with an experienced esthetician who is also knowledgeable in nutritional skincare and gut health. Review of your current homecare should be part of the evaluation.

Having professional deep cleansing facials, chemical and or physical exfoliation, LED light therapy combined with proper, daily home care have proven to be greatly beneficial in treating acne. Professional facials offer the dissolving and removal of hardened sebum in the follicle which, if left untreated, would ultimately lead to inflammation and potential post-inflammatory hyperpigmentation (PIH). PIH can also be caused by squeezing, scabbing, and irritating the blemish. It is best to leave it alone and have it professionally treated for quicker healing without the risk of becoming hyperpigmented.

Acne on other parts of the body such as the chest and back is usually a sign of a more systemic condition. Again, taking a closer look at diet and lifestyle can help determine the proper approach. Please see our earlier chapter on nutritious eating. If you are still struggling, working with a wellness coach, nutritionist or an esthetician who is well-versed in proper diet and nutrition in relation to skin health is beneficial.

ACNE HOME-CARE TIPS

- Do not squeeze or try to extract impurities yourself.

- Reduce inflammation with warm compresses. This can lessen the potential for post-inflammatory hyperpigmentation and soften blemishes.

- Use proper skincare, including gentle exfoliation, at home.

- LED light therapy at home can assist with quicker healing.

- Drink a lot of water, and eat nutritious food including fruits and vegetables. Test how reducing or cutting out sugar, dairy, alcohol, and/or meat and shellfish can help reduce breakouts.

- Keep a food diary to see any patterns you may notice that could be triggers.

- Consider the level of stress in your life and look for ways to de-stress and calm.

HYPERPIGMENTATION

Hyperpigmentation or darkened areas of the skin, is another quite common condition of the skin where many people seek professional assistance. It is the excessive production of melanin (or color pigment) causing dark spots anywhere on the body, including the skin of the face, hands, chest, back, and legs and can vary in size.

CAUSES OF HYPERPIGMENTATION

Hyperpigmentation is caused by the excess production of melanin by the melanocytes in the basal layer of the epidermis. Several things can stimulate excessive production of melanin by the melanocytes.

- UVA and UVB rays
- Hormones, including oral contraceptives, and pregnancy
- Injury or trauma which causes inflammation
- Some medications side effects and those that increase your sensitivity to sunlight
- Areas of constant friction such as the elbows and knees

Think of the melanocytes as a little army coming out to protect your internal organs from the invasion: it is really a defense mechanism. So, concerning acne, it is the inflammation or trauma and the bacteria that are causing the melanocytes to come out and protect the skin.

SUN DAMAGE IN DEPTH

Hyperpigmentation from sun exposure is the result of excessive contact with the sun's ultraviolet rays leading to inflammation. Melanin absorbs UV waves to prevent DNA damage to the keratinocytes. There are mainly two types of ultraviolet rays, UVA and UVB that affect the skin. UVA rays are the longest, and they make up most of the UV radiation that reaches the earth's surface. UVA rays are equally intense throughout the day and are just as strong in winter as they are during the summer months. They pass through clouds and even glass windows on a hazy day, penetrating deep into the dermal layer.

UVB rays, which are responsible for the burning of our skin, are the most intense when the sun is at its highest point in the sky, which is between 10:00 AM and 4:00 PM. They are blocked somewhat by the ozone layer.

Ironically, tanning booths filter out the majority of the B rays and primarily use the A rays, so they are more damaging than natural sunlight. The World Health Organization's International Agency for Research on Cancer (IARC) classifies tanning beds and lamps in its highest cancer risk category ("carcinogenic to humans") — the same category as other hazardous substances such as plutonium and certain types of radium.

The Melanoma Research Foundation states that people who use tanning beds are at a much greater risk for developing all types of cancer, including melanoma. Some reports estimate that the risk increases by 75% for people who use a tanning bed before the age of 35.

The difference between UVA and UVB is that UVA is more damaging and cancer-causing, and UVB is responsible for burning and inflammation, which can lead to discoloration. Because UVA rays are the longest, they penetrate the dermal layer where they affect the DNA of cells. After sun exposure, the skin darkens by increasing melanin production to absorb the UV radiation and protect itself. A tan is your skin's defense against DNA damage to the cells.

How long a tan lasts after sun exposure depends on the type of exposure to UV light that was received and the length of time that you are out in the sun. UVA rays penetrate deeper into the dermis, producing immediate skin darkening after only a few minutes of exposure which can last for a few days. Exposure to UVB is a little delayed in showing up but persists for longer and is more deeply embedded into the skin.

On the bright side, sunlight does have health benefits. Regular sun exposure is the most natural way to get enough vitamin D. We only need 10-to-30 minutes of midday sunlight, several times per week. This is enough sunlight to transform fats under the skin into vitamin D.

This helps your body absorb calcium for stronger bones and improve various skin and hair issues that are triggered by a deficiency in vitamin D. Additionally, a study conducted in the U.K. showed that a dose of UV-equivalent sunlight of 30 minutes could significantly lower blood pressure (also known as hypertension).

Eating foods that are rich in beta-carotene such as oranges, carrots, and sweet potatoes can help protect us from sun damage. Beta-carotenes also suppress inflammation.

A healthy dose of sunlight is okay; you just have to be aware of how long you are out, and when the sun's rays are at their peak and most damaging. This will allow you to take the necessary precautions to prevent damage and reap the rewards when it is safer. Remember your exposure time should depend on how sensitive your skin is to sunlight, and that medications can also affect this.

TREATING HYPERPIGMENTATION

Hyperpigmentation from acne can be readily corrected with the appropriate skincare regimen. Homecare should include lactic acid exfoliation, Vitamin C skin brightening, Vitamin A, and tyrosinase-suppressing ingredients like Kojic Acid, Vitamin C, Azelaic Acid to slow down melanin production and brighten discoloration for an even skin tone. A series of gentle, professional chemical exfoliation treatments can be greatly beneficial.

Wearing sun protection daily while being treated is very important to assist your progress and reduce recurrence. Personally, I do not recommend the use of hydroquinone. It is thought to be a carcinogenic or cancer causing chemical, can cause skin sensitivity and dryness and even cause discolorations in some individuals with darker complexions. Some studies have also reported abnormal function of the adrenal glands and high levels of mercury in people who have used hydroquinone containing ingredients. Hydroquinone has already been banned in Japan, the European Union, and Australia.

AGING SKIN

There are two primary causes of aging: intrinsic (genetically determined) and extrinsic (UV and toxic exposure) aging. According to the American Academy of Dermatology, intrinsic factors (based on what we inherit in our DNA and genes) are responsible for only 10% of what we see as signs of aging skin. This is the natural process of skin aging due to internal influences. On the other hand, 90% of visible aging is extrinsic.

Extrinsic aging is how our skin ages due to external factors and lifestyle, which we have absolute control over. This includes ultraviolet radiation, UVA and UVB light, cigarette smoke (both inhaled and second-hand), a nutrient-poor diet (especially lacking in vitamin A, C, E, and folic acid) excess alcohol consumption, stress, harsh scrubs or over-exfoliation, lack of sleep, and environmental toxins such as air pollution. All of these things cause free radical damage. Extrinsic aging is the complete opposite of a healthy lifestyle.

Free radicals are unstable molecules that can damage our skin. They are unstable because they are missing one or two electrons, and so they try to bond with other atoms or molecules in an effort to stabilize. Since skin is our largest organ and exposed to the elements, it is vulnerable to free radicals. As they try to bond with other molecules, free radicals can cause oxidative stress, which harms DNA and can weaken living cells and tissues.

To help protect your body and avoid free-radical damage, researchers recommend avoiding the following:

- Air pollution
- Sunlight (UV radiation) in excess
- Smoking
- Alcohol
- Pesticides and other harmful chemicals
- Poor nutrition
- Too much stress

There is a beautiful example of the differences between intrinsic and extrinsic aging in a well-known image of a 69-year-old gentleman who has spent 28 years traveling cross-country as a delivery truck driver. The left side of his face is significantly more wrinkled and has a leathery texture with deep lines and sagging, in comparison to the right side of his face. It is a great demonstration of the damage the sun's ultraviolet radiation can cause to a person's skin. The result is premature aging, more wrinkles, and an increased risk of skin cancer. See the image here: https://tinyurl.com/tpuhwuj.

Another very good example of extrinsic aging is of a set of 61-year-old identical twins who lived very different lives in different parts of the country. While one lived in the Northeast, the second one lived in Southern Florida. One of the sisters spent a significantly greater amount of time in the sun without the use of sunscreen and smoked, while the other sister did not. The sister who spent more time outside and smoked had many more wrinkles, loss of elasticity, and hyperpigmentation on her face. See the images here: https://tinyurl.com/qqeyu49

ENVIRONMENTAL DAMAGE
AND SKIN AGING

Environmental damage is caused by external conditions and it affects how we look and feel and impacts the health of our skin. This comes from air pollution, sun exposure, computer screens, lighting, and more. It can be a significant underlying factor in many skincare problems.

Of growing concern over recent years is the effect of air pollution on our skin. Air pollution, also known as particulate matter or particle pollution, is another cause of extrinsic aging and it is more prevalent in urban environments. It is a mix of solid and liquid droplets floating in the air, according to the Environmental Protection Agency.

Air pollution can come in the form of dirt, manufacturing dust, soot, or smoke that we breathe in as we inhale. Particulate pollution also comes from coal-and-natural gas-fired plants, car emissions, factory chemicals, manufacturing dust, pollen, and even molds.

It has been shown to cause greater amounts of redness in the skin, acne flare-ups, inflammation and increased free radicals. When there is an imbalance of free radicals and antioxidants in the body this is known as oxidative stress. This leads to cell and tissue damage accelerating the aging process. Long term oxidative stress is believed to contribute to the development of chronic health conditions such as cancer, diabetes, and even heart disease.

There is a direct correlation between what we do or did not do to take care of our body and our skin, how our lifestyle and the environment affects us, and how our skin looks and we physically feel today.

Extrinsic or environmental damage can be improved by working with a professional esthetician and wellness professional who can guide you in the right direction. Knowing your concerns and the outcome you want to achieve will determine what treatments, home skincare products and lifestyle adjustments are needed to achieve optimal results. Boosting antioxidants both topically and internally coupled with stimulating and reparative treatments are top priorities.

UNDERSTANDING INTRINSIC AGING

Using proper skin care, coupled with professional treatments, can help improve the negative effects of extrinsic aging. This shows up on our skin as brown spots, leathery texture, and horizontal and vertical lines. But what about intrinsic aging? The natural aging process (which is intrinsic aging) results in the loss of volume in the mid-face due to the subcutaneous tissue thinning out.

The first layer of skin known as the epidermis becomes sluggish, and the cell renewal process slows down. The migration of healthy cells moving up from the bottom basal layer to the top stratum corneum is not happening as quickly as it has in the past, leading to dullness, dehydration, and a rough texture.

The second layer of the skin (the dermis, where the collagen and elastin fibers are found) gets broken down or torn apart primarily because of the oxidative stress that is a result of extrinsic aging but can also happen from intrinsic. It provides less support due to the breaking down and flattening of the fibrous structure of collagen and elastin.

Additionally, we will lose volume and plumpness due to a thinning of the subcutaneous tissue. The mid-face, just below the orbital ridge of our eyes, is where we typically see the most loss of volume, giving us a flattened-out appearance. We start to notice jowls along the jawline and the nasolabial fold begins to form a crease from the corner of our nose going down to the corners of our mouth. It becomes more prominent because of the changing internal structure.

It's easy to visualize if you think about a table that has a tablecloth draped over it: over time, the table gets smaller, but the tablecloth remains the same size. You will then have excess cloth pooling on the floor. Your skin becomes too large for the underlying structure. This is known as intrinsic aging.

CLEAN PRODUCTS

Understanding how the skin functions, and then choosing the appropriate skincare products for home use, can allow you to take control over the health of your skin and how it ages. With so many options available, choosing the right products is critical and can have an impact on not only the health of your skin, but your body as a whole.

Surprisingly, the FDA does not currently regulate what goes into personal and beauty-care products, so what you put on your skin may not be good for your health. Any current cosmetic regulations that are in place are more than 81 years old. While the European Union has banned more than 1,000 chemicals in personal care products, currently the United States has only banned 11. If a product is intended to be used daily and it stays on our body all day long like a deodorant, or a moisturizer, we should be looking for clean and safe options. Clean beauty can have a wide range, but there are some ingredients that should be absolutely avoided.

In our spas, we recommend using products that are clean and free of harmful or suspected toxic ingredients, that are not tested on animals, and are created with mindfully selected ingredients that are ethically sourced, and made with our health and care of the environment in mind.

WHAT IS A CLEAN PRODUCT?

The goal of skincare products today is to get results, and we are making products to reach the deeper layers of the skin so they can be the most effective in treating the skin and achieving those results. Therefore, if you're using active ingredients, you want to make sure that what you're putting on is going to be clean and without any negative impact.

The most common ingredients of concern and why:

Alcohols such as methanol, isopropyl alcohol, propanol, benzyl alcohol, and SD alcohol can cause irritation, inflammation, and free-radical damage. They are also very drying and disrupt the skin barrier.

- Parabens, a chemical preservative and microbial – Studies show parabens mimic estrogen in the body and there is evidence linking them to reproductive organ harm, thyroid disruption, hormone related cancers, and obesity. Even early onset of puberty in girls according to a study published by Human Reproduction, due to the use of parabens through beauty products.

- Phenoxyethanol, also called Ethylene Glycol Monophenyl Ether, is a preservative with antibacterial properties. Likely made in a laboratory by treating phenol (created from benzene) with ethylene oxide. Used as a safer alternative to Paraben preservatives however, according to the Material Safety Data Sheet on phenoxyethanol, it is quickly absorbed into the skin and is known to cause irritation to both the skin, lungs and potentially the kidneys. In an article published October 2019, in the Journal of European Academy of Dermatology, it is said to be used in personal care products at a concentration of less than 1%, however, rarely is it taken into account that it is used in many products and cumulatively likely to exceed the recommended 1% limit. Many women use a minimum of

13 personal care products daily. In this same article, the French National Agency for the Safety of Medicines and Health Products (ANSM) recommend that phenoxyethanol should not be used as a preservative in cosmetic products intended for application on children 3 years and under.[1]

- Chlorphenesin is a synthetic preservative that has been linked to moderate skin irritation. The ingredient is currently restricted in Japan, as it has been associated with allergic dermatitis, immunosuppressive qualities, and has been found to be harmful if swallowed or inhaled.[2]

- Sulphates (Ethoxylated agents), are responsible for the bubbles and lather in a product like shampoo or cleansers, derived from petroleum and sulfur, and has been found to strip hair and the skin's natural acid mantle. The Environmental Protection Agency (EPA) lists it as a known carcinogenic.

- Phthalates, a group of chemicals that make products more pliable and help fragrances – are known endocrine disruptors and are linked to reproductive harm in

---

[1] https://cosmeticobs.com/en/articles/ansm-47/ansm-a-mandatory-warning-on-leave-on-cosmetics-containing-phenoxyethanol-4720
https://www.officinea.fr/le-blog/en/phenoxyethanol-7-reasons-to-banish-it/

[2] Japan Ministry of Health, Labour and Welfare. 2006. Standards for Cosmetics. Evaluation and Licensing Division. Pharmaceutical and Food Safety Bureau. Cosmetic Ingredient Review (CIR) 2020. CIR Assessments. Appears as: ; Chemical_Name: CHLORPHENESIN; ; CAS: 104-29-0; Classification: QQQ01;

children and men. Some phthalates, like dibutyl phthalate (DBP), have been classified by The State of California and other authoritative bodies as a reproductive and developmental toxicant, and the European Union banned the use of this ingredient in cosmetics and personal care products.[3]

- Fragrances or perfumes typically contain Phthalates and other toxic chemicals – they are known irritants and can trigger allergies and asthma.

- Formaldehydes, most notorious preservative used in history – recognized in 2015 by the American Contact Dermatitis Society as Contact Allergen of the Year. It is also globally known as a carcinogenic that can also cause nosebleeds, itchy eyes and sore throat.

- Benzene ethanal which has been shown to have negative effects on our brains and nervous systems.

- Alcohols such as methanol, isopropyl alcohol, propanol, benzyl alcohol and SD alcohol, can cause inflammation

---

[3] https://www.ewg.org/skindeep/ingredients/701929-DIBUTYL_PHTHALATE/
European Commission. 2013. Cosing, the European Commission database with information on cosmetic substances and ingredients. Accessed on March 1, 2013 at http://ec.europa.eu/consumers/cosmetics/cosing/ .
California EPA (California Environmental Protection Agency). 9/2008. Office of Environmental Health Hazard Assessment. Safe Drinking Water and Toxic Enforcement Act of 1986. Chemicals known to the State to cause cancer or reproductive toxicity.

and free-radical damage. They are also very drying and disrupt the skin barrier.

- Hydroquinone, a common skin lightening ingredient to treat discoloration – linked to cancer, decreased immune response and abnormal function of the adrenal glands. The European Union as well as Japan and Australia have banned this ingredient.

- Polyethylene glycols (or "PEGs") are petroleum compounds composed of condensed ethylene oxide and water that can have various derivatives and functions, and in certain forms can cause system toxicity and are known carcinogens.[4]

- Refined Petroleum (mineral oil and paraffin), is a widely used moisturizing agent found in creams and lip balms – Not only is it important to avoid it from an environmental standpoint but the World Health Organization listed it as a carcinogenic and 2011 publication in NCBI PubMed listed mineral oil to be the greatest contaminant of the human body.

---

[4] https://www.ncbi.nlm.nih.gov/pmc/articles/PMC4505343/

- Propylene glycol and butylene glycol, are chemicals used to enhance absorption found in shampoos, conditioners, soap, and moisturizers, have been linked to cancer and endocrine disruption and organ toxicity. Propylene glycol is a small organic alcohol commonly used as a skin conditioning agent and has been associated with irritant and allergic contact dermatitis as well as contact urticaria in humans; these sensitization effects can be manifested at propylene glycol concentrations as low as 2%.[5]

- Silica, used as an absorbent and anti-caking ingredient found in cosmetics and bath products - are not biodegradable therefore harmful to the environment and are known carcinogens.

- Talc, used in face powders and eye shadows – typically is not purified and can be contaminated with asbestos, a known carcinogenic. In Dec. 2018, Reuters published an investigation that found baby powder products by Johnson & Johnson linked to cases of ovarian cancer and mesothelioma.

---

[5] https://www.ewg.org/skindeep/ingredients/705315-PROPYLENE_GLYCOL/
CIR (Cosmetic Ingredient Review) 2006. CIR Compendium, containing abstracts, discussions, and conclusions of CIR cosmetic ingredient safety assessments. Washington DC.
EC (Environment Canada). 2008. Domestic Substances List Categorization. Canadian Environmental Protection Act (CEPA) Environmental Registry.

Our spa, Complexions Spa for Beauty and Wellness, is Gold Level LEED certified and registered with the US Green Building Council. We believe in the importance of being an eco-friendly facility, and we stand by that vision by having clean products that are going to be good for you holistically. As a result, we have created our own line of skincare products for the guests of the spa called Dubois Beauty, and we maintain strict requirements to provide effective, clinical products that achieve results using clean formulations.

CREATING A HEALTHY HOME ENVIRONMENT

Clean beauty personal care products and clean eating all make perfect sense. Fewer chemicals and toxins make you look and feel more vibrant and healthier. But what about our homes? Cleaning supplies, detergents, paints, contaminants, and products that we use every day can harm our health and the environment.

Scientific studies have shown that many harmful chemicals found in home cleaning products can be the underlying factor in autoimmune disorders, chronic dry or watery eyes, allergies, asthma, headaches, pain, and inflammation, and even contribute to fertility and hormone issues. Keeping your home free of harmful toxins can greatly impact your health.

Many generic cleaning products contain harmful toxic chemicals. You can begin a healthy home detox by switching to natural alternatives. Avoid products with warnings, hazard, or poison labels as well as ingredients like ammonia, DEA, APEs, TEA, and Sulfates. Instead, opt for plant-based ingredients and solvent and phosphate-free labels. You can also make your own cleaning supplies using baking soda, lemon, and vinegar combined with hot water, put in a glass spray bottle, and label.

Here are some ways to ensure your home is healthy and environmentally friendly:

- Leave your shoes at the door and not wearing footwear in the house

- Add indoor plants

- Open windows to allow for fresh outside air to circulate

- Let in the sunshine

- Use energy-saving light bulbs

- Use appliances efficiently and don't leave lights turned on while not in use

- Compost food scraps

- Conserve water by not leaving it running (for example, while washing dishes or brushing your teeth)

- Recycle your trash

- Use reusable and recyclable goods

- Eliminate plastics

- Be mindful of VOCs in paint, adhesive materials, and even candles or poor-quality essential oil.

DIY Recipes for Home Cleaning

There are a number of cleaning products that can be made easily at home with clean, green ingredients. To get started, we also recommend investing in a few reusable, environmentally friendly cleaning tools:

- Glass spray bottle

- Environmentally friendly sponges

- Natural scrub brushes

- Natural, lint-free microfiber cloths

- Wool dryer balls (to use instead of dryer sheets)

All-purpose Cleaner

- 2 cups distilled white vinegar
- 2 cups water
- 20-30 drops of essential oil such as lemon (optional)

Put the mixture in a glass spray bottle and label contents. Heating contents until warm in the microwave will increase cleaning performance.

Laundry Detergent

- 1 cup soap flakes (these can be made by grating your favorite pure vegetable soap with a cheese grater)
- 1 cup washing soda (sodium carbonate)
- 1 cup baking soda (sodium bicarbonate)

Mix ingredients together and store in a glass container. Use 1 tablespoon per load (2 tablespoons for heavily soiled laundry) wash in warm or cold water.

Bathroom Cleaner

- Baking soda
- Vinegar

Use baking soda instead of scouring powder. Sprinkle it on porcelain fixtures and rub with a wet sponge. Drizzle with vinegar and let soak and scrub with a toilet brush to remove any stains.

Window Cleaner

- 1/2 cup vinegar
- 1 quart warm water

Mix ingredients in a spray bottle and use on glass surfaces. Rub with a lint-free cloth and polish with wadded up newspaper. For dirty outdoor windows, wash with soapy water, rinse well, and squeegee dry.

HEALTHY AGE MANAGEMENT

"Healthy age management" is a term that I started using several years ago. As a practicing esthetician since 1984, I know that skincare is not just about a quick fix, it's a lifestyle. It is a balance between working with a professional esthetician who can prescribe the appropriate skincare for twice-daily home use, combined with professional in-office skin care procedures, and living beautifully.

"Nature gives you the face you have at twenty; it is up to you to merit the face you have at fifty."

— Coco Chanel

THE FOUR PILLARS OF SKINCARE

There are four pillars of skincare for optimal skin rejuvenation and healthy age management. They are:

- Gentle removal of dead skin (Exfoliation)

- Use of antioxidants and anti-inflammatory ingredients (Preserving)

- Stimulation and repair of cell function (Restoring)

- Proper hydration and adequate sun protection (Protecting)

If we look back to how the skin functions and how we are aging, these four pillars are what we need to focus on. So we will start with **exfoliation**. As we age, healthier cells develop in the basal layer and migrate to the surface of the epidermis known as the stratum corneum. They begin as nice, plump cells filled with moisture and as they migrate up to the surface, they become flattened scales of epidermal cells.

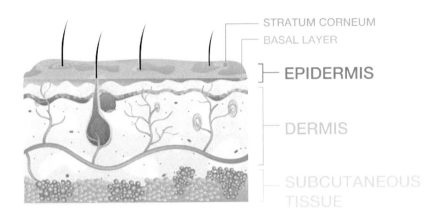

STRATUM CORNEUM
BASAL LAYER

EPIDERMIS

DERMIS

SUBCUTANEOUS
TISSUE

When we are young, this migration happens very quickly, and as we age that process begins to slow down. A good example of this is that when a baby falls and gets a scrape, the wound heals rather quickly, almost overnight. However, if an elderly person has bumped their arm, it can take up to 10 days or even two weeks to heal. That is because the cell renewal process has slowed down dramatically. In healthy, younger skin, it takes approximately 28 days for the cells to form in the basal layer and work their way up to the surface. As we age, this process slows down greatly to between 28 and 45 days.

Due to this slowing cell-renewal process, **exfoliation** becomes important to eliminate that layer of dead skin on the surface. If left alone, it would lead to a dull and dry skin appearance with fine lines and discoloration. These dead skin cells are held there by intercellular lipids similar to glue. The dead cells stay on the skins surface for a longer time, and therefore skin looks dull, is not hydrated, and has a texture that is rough to the touch. Gentle exfoliation will loosen and dissolve the glue-like lipid that bonds the dead skin cells to the surface, sloughing them off, and exposing younger, fresher, more hydrated skin cells.

The next critical step is **preserving** the skin using antioxidants to protect against long term oxidative stress mainly caused from extrinsic impact. The free radicals damage healthy skin cells, proteins and DNA which triggers the inflammatory response. Inflammation causes more free radical damage creating a vicious cycle contributing to an accelerated aging. Antioxidants are critical in neutralizing or removing free radicals by donating an electron to negate this process. They help protect the body from oxidative stress. Important and powerful antioxidants include Vitamin A, C and E. These and additional antioxidants should be used as part of a regular program every morning.

The third step that we need to do is to restore the skin by **stimulating and repairing it.** With the application of controlled injury and incorporating cell nutrition, proteins, and amino acids, we can stimulate the regeneration and renewal of collagen and elastin. We can improve and rebuild what's been torn down from the extrinsic and intrinsic aging process. We can balance cell communication to normalize cell function, resulting in a healthier skin barrier.

In my opinion, Vitamin A is the most vital nutrient for balancing and repairing the skin. Due to environmental influences and our hectic, stressful lifestyles, this nutrient (along with others) is depleted daily and needs to be replenished every day. This is the root cause of an unhealthy complexion and many skin disorders. Vitamin A serums, as part of a daily skincare program is the best way to replenish the skin of this critical nutrient.

Vitamin A is a cell communicator that regulates normal cell function and helps them to act in a healthy, younger way. Some of these benefits include balancing sebum production to reduce oiliness and improve acne conditions, it has been scientifically shown to stimulate fibroblast cells, responsible for producing collagen and improving the skin tone and texture.

Vitamin A also improves the appearance of hyperpigmentation by inhibiting tyrosinase enzyme which is found in human melanocytes and responsible for stimulating the production of melanin. Vitamin A supports the skin's immune response and assists the skin in wound healing and natural moisturizing. All these conditions are associated with the appearance of aging skin which every skin type will benefit by its daily use. This will result in improving the health of your skin giving it a radiant and glowing complexion.

And then lastly is the step to **hydrate and protect** skin. Hydrated skin cells are filled with moisture and are smooth and soft. As we age, our estrogen is depleted and our skin becomes drier, so we need to keep our epidermal cells plumped up with moisture to prevent dehydration.

Think of dehydration as grapes shriveled up into raisins. We need to prevent this dehydration by keeping the skin cells filled with moisture. It is important not to use harsh cleansers that dehydrate and deplete the skin, and also to replenish the skin with moisture-binding, ingredient-rich moisturizers, which will help smooth and soften your skin.

Ideally, your daily daytime moisturizer should include sun protection factors to protect the skin from collagen and elastin deterioration and hyperpigmentation. If it does not than separate sun protection should be layered over your moisturizer.

THE TRUTH ABOUT SUNSCREEN

In my experience, most people do not understand the importance of using sun protection to protect the body from the harmful effects of UV rays. Our body's defense against these damaging rays results in thickened and darker skin. A tan is not your friend, it is a reaction to these damaging rays and the source of free radical damage.

Although melanin becomes protective, it is the process of producing the tan that causes the damage. Our melanocytes produce more granules of melanin to absorb and scatter the UV radiation. Melanin is most protective against UVB rays and unfortunately, UVA rays still penetrate deeper causing more damage and they also activate free radicals leading to skin aging and skin cancers.

UV light is just as strong in the winter months as it is during the summer months, and it penetrates glass when you are driving in the car or sitting next to a window. Eighty percent of the sun's rays can still penetrate on a cloudy hazy day so do not be fooled by a cloudy sky. We also receive UV damage from fluorescent light bulbs as well as the blue light from our computer screens, tablets, and smartphones.

Sun protection needs to be applied every day as part of a daily morning ritual. When headed out for extended periods of outdoor activity like going to the beach or a round of golf, it should be applied liberally approximately 20 minutes ahead of time. It is suggested to minimize excessive sun exposure during the mid-day peak hours of ten and three.

Look for broad-spectrum sun protection that will protect against both UVA and UVB rays. Know the difference between types of ingredients that offer protection, physical protection and chemical protection. The main difference lies in the way they protect the skin from UV rays. Physical sunscreen ingredients help block the UV rays by forming a physical shield that reflects rays away from the skin. Whereas a sunscreen that contains chemical ingredients absorbs the UV rays minimizing their ability to pass through into the skin.

Keep in mind, no sunscreen ingredient is 100% effective at blocking the UV rays. In fact, the Food and Drug Administration banned the term "sunblock" because it created a false sense of protection to consumers.

I personally prefer using a mineral sunblock which is also safe for our oceans and reefs. Some sunscreen ingredients, such as Oxybenzone (Benzophenone-3) and octinoxate can stop the growth of green algae, accumulate in coral tissues, harm young animals, and disrupt the reproductive systems in mussels, sea urchins, fish, and dolphins.

Safe mineral ingredients include (non-nano) titanium dioxide and zinc oxide. A mineral sunscreen sits on the surface of the skin and tends to be a safe option for even the most sensitive skin types. Whereas UV absorbing chemicals in sunscreen can be irritating and cause allergic reactions in some individuals.

It is also important to understand what "SPF" means. SPF is a rating of the "Sun Protection Factor." This number reflects how long a sun protection product protects the skin from burning, largely the UVB rays. For example, if your skin would normally burn after ten minutes in the sun, an SPF 30 sun protection product should allow you to stay in the sun without burning for approximately three hundred minutes.

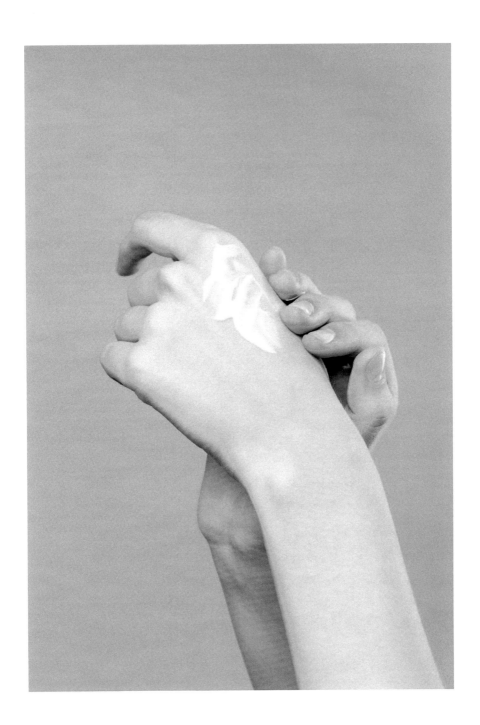

If you have fairer skin and would normally burn after five minutes, an SPF 30 sunscreen should allow you to stay in the sun for about one hundred fifty minutes. It's important to point out that swimming and perspiring break down the sun protection ingredients despite their SPF number and it should be reapplied more frequently due to that. It's a safe assumption to reapply approximately every two hours for most people.

All sunscreens are required to have an SPF number. Many scientists do not recommend the higher SPF numbers because there is a minimal advantage or greater protection but there is a much greater risk of sensitivity due to the higher chemical content. Additionally, some of those ingredients can themselves be converted to free radicals by exposure to UV rays.

I suggest looking for sun protection that contains antioxidants as part of the formula or adding it before your sunscreen application. Antioxidants are free radical scavengers that help to neutralize the damaging effects of the UV rays. They can also be applied after sun exposure, even sunburned skin, to help reduce redness and inflammation. Our clothing is also a good source of adequate protection, such as long sleeve, lightweight swim shirts, sunglasses, and of course hats.

BODY CARE

Body care covers a wide range of activities to help relax, restore, and rejuvenate your body. From morning to night, here are a few body-care techniques you can incorporate into your daily, weekly, or monthly regimen.

DRY BRUSHING

Dry brushing is the act of brushing your dry skin with a natural bristled brush. It is recommended before you take a shower, as a way of gently exfoliating dead skin. I suggest using a dry brush with a handle to care for hard-to-reach areas. Begin at your feet, and working up in light, circular motions moving inward toward the heart. You can go a little deeper for rough patches of skin on places such as elbows, knees, and feet. It also increases circulation. When you increase circulation, you help bring oxygen and nutrients to the cells providing a nice glow to your skin.

If you haven't tried it before, start slowly — maybe once a week. If you have sensitive skin, especially psoriasis or eczema, proceed with care. Once you see how your skin feels and reacts, you can ramp up to a few times per week.

Follow dry brushing with a shower and a natural body oil or lotion.

HYDROTHERAPY

Hydrotherapy is the practice of using water for treatment and pain relief. Water treatments can be done at a spa or at home, and popular hydrotherapies include:

- Watsu: massage therapy while floating in a warm water pool

- Compresses: towels soaked in cool or warm water to treat body pains (cool compresses reduce inflammation and swelling; warm compresses promote blood flow and soothe sore muscles)

- Balneotherapy: warm-water baths with beneficial salts, minerals, oils, or herbs

- Steam baths: steam rooms filled with warm, humid air and in some cases essential oils are difused

- Contrast hydrotherapy: alternating between hot and cool temperatures during a shower, or switching from hot steam baths to cool pools

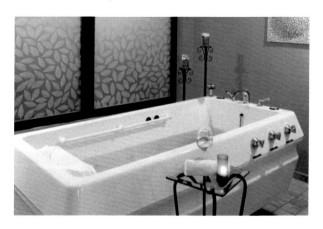

Look for spa treatments that combine the beneficial treatments of water therapies with massage or other treatments. For example, a warm-bath soak followed by a healing massage can reduce muscle pain and boost immune strength.

To create an at-home bath treatment, try adding any of the following to a warm-water bath. (You can also pair these for additional benefits):

- Epsom salts (actually a mineral compound of magnesium and sulfate): add 1 to 2 cups five minutes before you get in the bath to ease sore muscles, pain, and inflammation

- Essential oils: add a few drops of your favorite aromatherapeutic oils to balance and soothe the mind and body

- Coconut oil: add 1 to 2 tablespoons for overall body hydration and replenishment

- Oatmeal: soak 1 to 2 cups in warm water for five minutes, then add to a bath to help reduce skin irritation and inflammation

BODY TREATMENTS

Body treatments let you care for the skin on your body with the same attention you give to the skin on your face. Just like your face, your body is exposed to environmental factors and UV rays. Using gentle cleansers, exfoliants, and protective moisturizers help reduce the appearance of aging. Exposed skin in particular needs more attention and protection: areas like the neck, chest, hands, and arms.

Look for a simple body-care regimen you can do in the bath or shower. Pick a gentle, sulfate-free body cleanser. Use a gentle exfoliating salt or sugar scrub with a buffer one-to-two times a week. Moisturize daily with a clean body oil and/or body moisturizer to help seal in hydration. You can also treat breakouts, discoloration, or patches of dryness with the appropriate skincare for extra impact. Follow with sunscreen on exposed areas.

CLEAN PRODUCTS AND BODY CARE

While many people understand the importance of clean and natural skincare for the face, the body is often ignored. We know that the skin is the largest organ of the body. However, your face is about 9% of the skin exposed on your body. For the rest, there are the same benefits to clean skincare, and choosing clean body-care products can have a big impact on the chemicals and ingredients your body absorbs.

PROFESSIONAL TREATMENTS

A NOTE FROM DR. WILLIAM DELUCA, BOARD CERTIFIED PLASTIC SURGEON

Although the purpose of this book is to facilitate a healthy and natural lifestyle, plastic surgery certainly has its legitimate place in helping us to look as young as we feel. Many of us realized the necessity of getting back in shape, losing those unwanted pounds, and pushing back the hands of time.

We can benefit both physically and emotionally from well thought out and appropriately applied plastic surgery procedures. The excesses of Hollywood are not the goal of most plastic surgeons. We want patients to look better, but not different.

Women after pregnancy and breastfeeding, for example, can combine the corollaries of healthy living with a little help from the surgical knife to achieve a flatter belly or firmer breasts. It can certainly be a mental defeat to do all of the right things with diet, exercise, and proper skincare and not be completely satisfied with the person looking back in the mirror.

In my 35 years of practice as a plastic surgeon, there has been a slow but steady evolution in our specialty. As with most surgical disciplines, it was symptom- and problem-oriented without concentrating on the individual as a whole. For the best practitioners, this was not enough and now are more "holistic" in their approach to their patients. What happened?

We realized that treating the aging process is not just removing sagging skin with a nip here and a tuck there, but evaluating the whole process within the entire aging process that is impacted by lifestyle and nutrition with our patients.

When I first entered plastic surgery, even until more recently, our approach to aging was aggressive, surgical procedures. At society meetings, it was one-upmanship to see who could stretch surgical limits, misunderstanding what natural beauty truly entailed.

Facelifts became ever more aggressive and unnatural. Lasers and aggressive peels came along, and we would then damage the skin just short of irreparable injury and softening wrinkles, creating an unnatural appearance and changes in skin pigmentation including hyper and hypopigmentation. The wrong buttons for healing were generally pulled. This, fortunately, is, for the most part, history. Good surgeons learn from experience and the results.

As with most technology after repeated use and unfortunate complications, the proper criteria are developed. Less and natural is replacing more and unnatural. We are returning to the old surgical admonition first, do no harm. As science and technology continue to evolve, we understand the molecular basis of aging much better which will eventually be our focus.

My guess, surgery may eventually go the way of the Dodo bird, fortunately, after I have hung my shingle. Today surgeons work closely with skincare professionals to formulate the best program for their patients. The knife is now not the first and only option for our patients, just another arrow in the quiver.

We rely more and more on gentle peels, injectable, and less invasive lasers, particularly in younger individuals. Moreover, in our fast-paced twenty-first-century lifestyle, downtime is at a premium

That being said, if a patient needs a facelift to correct their issues even using an excessive amount of fillers, etc., will not give them an ideal result. Just look at *People* magazine.

When surgery is the appropriate course, we now prepare the patient with proper nutrients and pre-op care. This continues in the post-operative period and as well as long term to achieve optimum results. Thus, a close working relationship with an experienced esthetician is a must. Patients heal faster, appreciate the care, concern, and know they have a support team during their plastic surgical journey.

As previously mentioned, the best way to maintain optimal surgical results is to continue with proper, clean skincare as well as making healthy lifestyle choices that are put forth in this comprehensive book.

SPAS

WHAT IS A SPA?

A spa is a place devoted to overall wellbeing through a variety of professional services that encourage the renewal of mind, body, and spirit.

Spas have become a way of life for many people and now you can find one in every city. It is a word used very freely in the industry, and it is important to understand the different kinds of spas available today to determine which one is best for you.

There are two theories about the origin of the word "spa," and both are centered on the idea of health and healing from centuries ago. One is that it is a Latin acronym, where "spa" stands for "solace per aqua" or "health from water." The other is that the word comes from the name of a small village in Belgium called "Spau," where Roman soldiers went to the waters to restore their aching muscles and heal their battle wounds.

There is a long history of spas or spa-like spaces. Hippocrates (460-370BC) thought all diseases were caused by an imbalance in the body. Romans were famous for building baths across their empire, and civilizations and cultures from all around the world took to the waters for healing. Going to the spa was part of one's lifestyle and families and friends spent time together at the spa. It wasn't until spas reached America that they become more of a pampering indulgence. The focus was less about wellness and more about the rich and famous going to indulge.

Today, however, that has changed and once again the focus is about health and wellbeing. People now understand the effects of stress on the body and how it impacts our health. The spa industry is returning to the very core of its beginnings, promoting wellness in ways we've seen traditionally and now adding new advances in healing, science, and technology.

WHO GOES TO SPAS?

The spa industry is seeing a steady growth in attendance and locations across the country. According to research conducted by Price Waterhouse Cooper on behalf of ISpa, in 2016, there were nearly 22,000 spas in the United States, servicing more than 180 billion visits each year. This growth includes both men and women seeking professional quality, result-oriented therapies to help them live a more balanced life.

The demographics of spa attendees are also changing. While women still account for most spa visits, recently male and youth attendance have increased. With more men attending spas, there has been a corresponding increase in male-focused spaces. Millennials with some disposable income, likely influenced by Boomer parents, are seeking spas to escape from work-related stress. Many spas offer teen-focused treatments, such as acne reduction. There is also an increasing space for younger populations, with spa services directed toward children's relaxation and wellbeing.

TYPES OF SPAS

There are many different types of spas available, and understanding the differences is important to ensure that you are getting the best results. There are destination spas, resort and hotel spas, and local day spas. There are "med spas," combining relaxation with medical treatments. There are also hair salons that have a room exclusively for facials and/or massage, and they, too, call themselves spas.

A "destination spa" is typically a resort where the main emphasis for the guest is on the spa. Offerings typically include spa services, workout facilities, outdoor activities, yoga, educational classes on wellness, and at times even cooking. Programs can range from a few days to a few months. It is designed to be truly an escape centered on wellbeing.

Another, quite different, type is a "resort spa." This type of location is a hotel that has a spa facility as one of its amenities. This type of spa is less focused on health. There is a big difference between the two types, as the former is centered around the spa and the latter is an added amenity people choose to participate in if they want a massage or facial during their vacation.

A "med spa" is a day spa associated with a medical doctor and incorporates the use of lasers and more advanced procedures. The service offerings tend to be more invasive and potentially require some healing time. A med spa usually also offers injectable treatments such as dermal fillers and neurotoxin skin treatments (such as Botox®, Dysport®, and Xeomin®). This type of procedure falls outside the scope of an esthetician and requires a licensed medical professional in most states. In some med spas, you will see some traditional spa services like massage therapy and facials; however, often they are in a more medical and less soothing environment.

A "day spa" can be a health and wellness center located in a place a client can go to regularly for maximum benefits. Day spas are also the most common type of spa. Rather than a longer-term visit to a destination spa or an indulgence while on vacation, a day spa can be integrated into one's lifestyle more easily. Some day spas are more focused on wellness, and others on pampering. Each day spa will offer different services, approaches to wellbeing, and treatments.

Services, comfort, and experience will vary based on location, but finding the right spa for you can be invaluable for your mental and physical health. Many combine destination, resort, and day-spa experiences and want guests to return. Building an ongoing customer-client relationship will maximize the benefits of treatments and remove any intake procedures that slow down that process. Regular access to spa treatments for continued health and wellbeing is considered a core part of living a holistic lifestyle.

KNOW YOUR GOAL WHEN YOU VISIT A SPA

Spas are filled with experts and are designed to promote wellbeing and relaxation. However, before arrival, visitors should ask themselves what they want to get out of the experience and their desired result. Is relaxation the primary goal? Do you want a specific treatment? Do you prefer a spa that encourages visitors to stay and relax or do you want to arrive, receive a treatment, and leave?

For the best experience, you should understand what you want from the visit before arrival. I recommend finding spas that encourage relaxation before and after any treatment procedures, to enhance the results achieved during the procedures and to fully enjoy a holistic lifestyle. Both the procedures themselves and the spa environment should reflect quality, calm, and service.

On arrival for the first appointment at any spa, you will be asked to fill out an intake form. This is an opportunity to share your desired goals for the visit. It also notifies your therapist of any conditions that could affect your experience in the spa. Candid communication between you and your therapist is critical. As the client, you should identify any goals, problems, injuries, or health concerns that could affect your treatment. Your therapist should guide you through the upcoming procedure, acknowledge your desired results, and make any recommendations for at-home care and follow-up appointments.

As part of professional training and licensing, every spa professional and the spa establishment, must follow state regulated requirements for proper cleaning, sanitizing, and disinfecting. As you look for a spa, make sure the facility adheres to and upholds these principles. Feel free to visit before you make an appointment and ask any questions you may have to address your concerns. In recent times, these standards have proven to be critical and a top priority for both the visitors of the spa and those who work there.

Often, visitors come to a spa hoping to address a specific concern or ailment. Spas are designed to address several issues. These include:

- Detoxes that will flush your system of accumulated toxins and pollutants that are caused by poor diet, eating habits, and the environment.

- A variety of massages that are designed for different results, such as muscle or stress relief.

- Hydrotherapy and saunas that can improve the immune system by reducing stress hormone levels in the body.

- Skin treatments that can reduce acne or rejuvenate skin to keep it looking youthful and bright.

- Exfoliation, skin smoothing, and nourishing.

The exact treatments offered will vary by spa location.

Determining why you want to go, what your goal is, and what you want to achieve will help you determine the best type of spa facility that offers the treatment experience that meets your needs. Understanding your own motivation for visiting a spa will help you find one that will allow you to get the most out of your experience.

HOW OFTEN SHOULD YOU VISIT A SPA?

The frequency of visits depends on the individual needs of the spa-goer. How often one receives a massage depends on the level of stress in the body and the desired goal. However, there are some general suggestions for how frequently to receive different types of treatments:

- Massage for general health: People with light-to-moderate stress levels should have a massage once or twice a month. People under high stress or in need of pain management may benefit from weekly massages or even a few times per week, depending on the level of discomfort. Frequency typically decreases over time and eventually people get to a maintenance level of going biweekly or monthly.
- Skincare: Treatment schedules will depend on the condition to be treated and the severity of the starting point. Whether treating acne, discoloration, aging skin, or even sensitivities, most people will benefit from treatments approximately two-to-four weeks apart. Determining the desired outcome will dictate the frequency of visits.
- Manicure and pedicure care and hair services are also most beneficial when received on a monthly maintenance schedule.

MASSAGE

Spa visits can provide an invaluable space to release everyday stresses, and studies have shown that massage therapy can provide relief to mental and physical conditions. Massage therapy is a technique to release muscular tension and restore physical and emotional wellbeing.

Massages can release cortisol, as well as lactic acid that gets trapped in the tender knots of taut, stressed muscles. They can also help improve circulation and pain relief, which can help alleviate stress-related conditions such as indigestion, chronic headache, anxiety, muscle tension, and back, shoulder, and neck pain.

SWEDISH MASSAGE

Swedish massage is maybe the most well-known massage technique. Designed to promote relaxation, Swedish massage uses long gliding movements to help relax the entire body. This is especially beneficial to reduce muscle toxins and improve circulation.

DEEP TISSUE THERAPEUTIC MASSAGE

Deep tissue massage is a more intensive massage treatment custom-tailored to specific areas of tension, soreness, and chronic discomfort. Moist heat and deep tissue techniques help improve flexibility and mobility in the muscle to unlock patterns of tension. These are designed for those seeking a firmer, more therapeutic treatment.

HOT STONE MASSAGE

This massage therapy treatment utilizes radiant heat from basalt river stones that penetrate deep into knots and tension, stimulating release and repair. Often paired with aromatic oils and a soothing massage technique, this massage helps rebalance and soothe. Himalayan salt stones can also be used in place of the basalt river stones for increased benefits from the therapeutic minerals found in the salt stones.

PRENATAL MASSAGE

Prenatal massages are specially designed to be safe and soothing to pregnant women. This massage can help soothe some of the discomforts that can accompany pregnancy, such as water retention, headaches, neck tension, cramping, stress, and soreness. Often, special massage beds, and/or pillows are used for increased comfort for the mother to be while enjoying the massage therapy.

FOREST BATHING MASSAGE

Inspired by the Japanese tradition of Shinrin-yoku (literally "Forest Air Bathing"), this massage therapy recreates the forest in your treatment room with appropriate essential oils from plants and trees to stimulate immunity and protect the lungs. It includes hot-towel compresses, flowing massage techniques, stretching movements to open joints, release tension, and loosen muscles. The health benefits include increased immune function, reduced stress levels, and lower blood pressure.

REFLEXOLOGY

Reflexology is based on the Chinese belief that qi (pronounced "chee") or "vital energy" underlies all body functions and flows through everyone. When you are under stress, this can cause an imbalance in the body and your qi becomes blocked, which can lead to illness. Reflexology is the massage technique that involves applying pressure to points on the body. These pressure points on the hands, feet, and ears are connected to different body systems and organs. In Chinese medicine, charts map this throughout the body. Applying pressure to these specific points releases blocked qi, keeping you balanced and your energy flowing. This is believed to have a wide range of health benefits, including disease prevention.

SHIATSU

Shiatsu is based on the holistic system of traditional Chinese medicine and is similar to reflexology in that they both aim to foster health and balance qi throughout the body. Shiatsu uses finger pressure along the long energy pathways (or "meridians") in much the same way as reflexology; however, it follows pathways that run the full length of the entire body — not just the hands, feet, and ears — to relieve blockages. The benefits of Shiatsu massage include relieving headaches, sleep disturbances, stress, tension, anxiety, chronic muscle pain and stiffness, and pregnancy discomfort. Overall, it promotes general health and wellness.

SKINCARE

We discussed the benefits of stress reduction and massage, so now we can review some of our most popular professional treatments for skincare, many of which are a combination of customized facial therapies. There is no "one size fits all" approach and treatments need to be personalized to address the root cause of an individual's particular skin condition. Combining different modalities also shows the most beneficial outcomes.

Many good options include nourishing facials, IPL, chemical exfoliation, micro-current, galvanic current, microdermabrasion, hydra facials, needling, and dermaplaning.

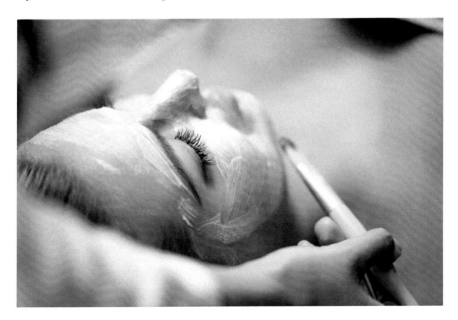

INTENSE PULSE LIGHT

IPL stands for Intense Pulse Light. It is a range of wavelengths of energy that is attracted to a specific target, specifically the capillaries and brown discolorations. It creates a gentle heat that coagulates the capillary wall, causing the collapse and reabsorption of the capillaries, thereby evening out redness over a few weeks. Heat is also absorbed into the melanin deposits, breaking up the brown spot and then gently exfoliating it away over seven-to-ten days.

The gentle heat (or "thermal injury") stimulates the fibroblast cells to produce more collagen and elastin. The controlled thermal injury puts your skin into a healing and rejuvenating phase. Ultrasound gel is applied to the skin with specific applicators that address redness or brown pigmentation. There is minimal downtime, and it is not necessary to be aggressive with this therapy to achieve ideal results. It is ideal to limit the amount of inflammation with any rejuvenation therapy.

DERMAL ROLLING AND MICRONEEDLING

Dermal needling (also known as collagen induction therapy) is another exceedingly popular treatment performed today.

This procedure involves pricking the skin multiple times with a specially designed device containing tiny needles to induce healing and cellular rejuvenation. The main objective is to create tiny micro-injuries that encourage the skin's wound healing response. This stimulates growth factors and cytokines for rejuvenation.

These micro-injuries also appear to reset or reboot cellular function, normalizing their action. Studies have shown that melanin distribution is evened out and sebaceous activity is balanced, improving acne conditions. The micro-channels created from the small punctures allow 80% more product to be absorbed into the skin (compared to the seven-to-10% with an application without dermal needling). Needling should always be used in conjunction with high-quality skincare nutrients applied to your skin after the treatment. Special attention should be made to be sure they are clean, safe products that are being applied.

Depending on the length of the needle, the treatment is considered cosmetic dermal rolling or medical microneedling. Typically, cosmetic dermal rolling is when the needles are .2mm and .3mm in length. Medical microneedling is done using needles from .5mm to 3.0mm. A topical numbing cream is usually needed due to greater sensitivity. Because our outermost layer of the skin, known as the epidermis, is generally thinner than a piece of paper, it is not necessary to be aggressive and go deep. Instead, multiple lighter treatments, in conjunction with quality skincare products used consistently, is what has the biggest impact and best results.

Not all needles are created equally and the material the needles are made of does make a difference. Titanium tends to hold its edge for longer-lasting sharpness. Cheaper brands are prone to needles falling out and bending easily. For home use, it is important to purchase a good quality roller. Also, keep in mind that personal-use rollers will need to be replaced frequently as the needles become dull after several uses.

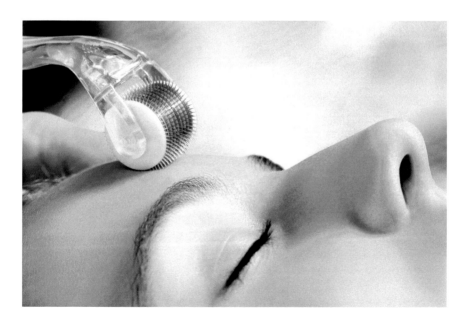

Getting Started

Preparing the skin with quality skincare before any treatment is essential to ensure the best results. Healthy skin will respond better, and the results will last longer. A good skin care regimen should include:

- Gentle cleanser and toner
- Mild exfoliators
- Topical antioxidants including vitamin C
- Topical vitamin A
- Topical copper peptides
- Topical growth factors
- Sun protection

A home-care dermal rolling treatment should take between two and 10 minutes. I recommend rolling at night and applying the appropriate serums immediately after the treatment followed by a moisturizer. The tiny micro-channels naturally close up within an hour, making it safe to apply mineral makeup the next morning.

Start rolling two times per week for two minutes, then three minutes three times per week, and building up to five to seven times per week. The goal is to establish a nighty regime of rolling followed by the application of nutrients. Rolling is safe to do on your neck and chest as well as on the back of your hands.

Steps

1. Cleanse and tone your skin and let it dry.
2. Divide the treatment area into sections: forehead, cheeks, eye area, nose, mouth area, and neck.
3. Hold the roller like a pen and with gentle pressure.
4. Roll repeatedly using short strokes back and forth, rather than long strokes. Do this three-to-four times.
5. Be sure to lift the roller frequently and change directions to avoid the needles creating tracks.
6. The direction should be up and down, back and forth, and diagonal.
7. Pull the skin down under the eye area so you are rolling along the orbital ridge.
8. Once rolling is complete, apply in your selected serum and allow it to dry.
9. Apply nighttime moisturizer.

Roller Maintenance

To disinfect the roller, you can rinse with soap and water. You can also drop a denture tablet on top of a cotton pad into a glass. Fill it with water and allow the roller to soak for 30 minutes. Denture tablets contain enzymes that will remove oils and bacteria. I do not recommend using alcohol to clean the roller; it can affect the glue used to assemble the roller, making the needles fall out. After cleaning, store it in a dry place.

CHEMICAL EXFOLIATION

Remember Samantha's chemical peel disaster on *Sex and the City*? The one that had Samantha hiding under a black veil and matching hat, hoping to shield the world from her irritated, red, peeling face? Yes, that scene. Just hearing the words "chemical peel" can be a little intimidating for most and can stop people from exploring this skincare option. It's time to demystify the "scary" chemical peel and learn the true benefits of this treatment.

A chemical peel is a form of exfoliation, which can benefit almost all skin types. Chemical exfoliation is a highly effective treatment for creating beautiful skin anywhere on the body, including the face, hands, neck, chest, back, and arms. It removes dead skin cells, reduces uneven pigmentation, increases hydration, diminishes large pores, and softens the appearance of fine lines and rough texture.

Our skin's surface, known as the stratum corneum, naturally renews itself approximately every 28 days by replacing dead cells on the surface of our skin. This process slows over time due to the normal aging process, as well as environmental damage. Chemical exfoliation is performed using a variety of solutions to loosen the dead layer of skin, causing it to shed. This controlled injury stimulates cells to produce more collagen and elastin restoring the skin's texture, improving tone and evening out color. Our collagen and elastin are what gives our skin a full, youthful appearance.

There are many different types of exfoliating and peeling agents ranging from fruit acid enzymes (such as papaya) which break down the keratin protein of the upper layers of the skin, to commonly used acids such as Alpha Hydroxy and Beta Hydroxy Acids (lactic, glycolic, and salicylic acid). All peels come in varying potency and PH levels, which increase or decrease penetration and irritation.

To see the best results — and keep those results — consistency and commitment are especially important. It is recommended to have a series of a minimum of six peels performed to start, every two-to-three weeks, depending on personal skin conditions. While you work your way through the series of peels, your esthetician will provide constant consultation, evaluation, and customization of the solutions based on your results. Once your series of peels is completed, maintenance should be done every four-to-six weeks. This can include incorporating fruit enzymes into a facial treatment to help provide long-lasting results.

You will experience minimal irritation and virtually no downtime while seeing maximum results. Your skin will look more radiant and luminous and will be less likely to show signs of discoloration and other imperfections.

To further the results and success of your chemical peel, a physical exfoliant can be used in conjunction with a chemical exfoliant. Physical exfoliants include a gentle buffing cream, dermaplaning and microdermabrasion. Adding a physical exfoliant into your treatment regimen can increase the penetration of your chemical peel, thus making it more effective.

One of the most important factors for achieving successful results with any type of treatment is to work with an experienced, well-trained esthetician. Estheticians help you get the most out of your chemical peel by providing a thorough consultation.

Your esthetician needs to know your goals, your current skincare routine, and any other procedures that you have had done. Telling your esthetician this background information is essential. They will then assess all these factors, and decide what peel is right for you, and how deep that peel should penetrate to achieve the desired result. Estheticians perform light-to-medium depth peels, while deeper peels that reach the dermal layer should be performed by a medical doctor. As always, remember aggressive treatments are not ideal and are absolutely not more affective.

DERMAPLANING

Dermaplaning is a safe, non-invasive treatment that uses an implement to gently remove dead skin cells and vellus hair. This is a wonderful form of exfoliation that can be performed as a stand-alone treatment or before other skin treatments.

Dermaplaning treatment is recommended to treat dry, rough skin, acne scars, uneven skin tone, large pores, fine lines, and even unwanted facial hair. Since the dermaplaning tool is a sharp blade, unwanted peach fuzz is eliminated during the treatment. In this manner, dermaplaning offers a rare combination of skin rejuvenation and facial- hair removal benefits. By removing vellus hair, oil buildup and dead skin that can block absorption, this safe and effective treatment promotes product penetration improving effectiveness of skin care products. Make up goes on ultra-smooth giving you a radiant glow.

Dermaplaning also has the added benefits of reducing the appearance of minor acne scars and wrinkles. It removes dead skin more swiftly and cleanly than the natural shedding process allows, so it can also trigger speedier skin cell turnover. Once you experience this treatment, you will be hooked, I guarantee it.

MICRODERMABRASION EXFOLIATION THERAPY

Microdermabrasion is a mechanical exfoliation that removes the uppermost layer of dead skin cells from the face, chest, and hands. It uses air pressure to circulate fine crystals over the skin to exfoliate the skin using a suction process that draws out debris and impurities.

This treatment uses no chemicals and is noninvasive on the skin. This process gently removes dead cells, oils, and other debris that clog pores and lead to aged and dull-looking skin. The results reveal the healthier and fresh skin below, thus rejuvenating the skin and providing a brighter skin complexion.

The procedure works in two parts. The first step is to use a mechanical device to gently exfoliate the skin surface. The second step removes dead skin cells using a vacuum system that clears away debris and skin cells.

Microdermabrasion is the perfect solution to treat all skin types and skin tones without creating any scarring or pigment changes. This treatment is less invasive than a traditional dermabrasion treatment and provides a faster recovery time.

MICROCURRENT FACIAL TREATMENTS

Microcurrent facial treatments have been used in medical applications since the 1970s. They incorporate the use of micro-ampere currents to stimulate adenosine triphosphate (ATP), the source of energy for all cells in the body that keeps everything going. As we age, we lose this energy.

This increased ATP energizes facial muscles, similar to how exercise energizes the muscles of our body. Because facial muscles are connected to the skin, the energized muscles result in a lifted appearance, known as a non-surgical facelift. The treatment is designed to soften fine lines and wrinkles and provide a lifted and rejuvenated appearance.

Professional microcurrent machines emit a positive and a negative current via two wands, probes, or sponges. When the probes are placed a few inches apart on the face, a circuit of current travels from one point to the other and stimulates the tissue in between. The current is sub-sensory, so all you feel is the gliding of the rods and a mild tingling sensation. The current is so gentle that clients often fall asleep during the treatment.

Microcurrent treatment can be used to improve:

- Muscle tone in the face and neck.
- The lift of jowls and eyebrows.
- The appearance of fine lines and wrinkles.
- Facial blood circulation.
- Lymphatic drainage.

GALVANIC CURRENT

Galvanic current, also known as direct current (DC), is a low-level, continuous current that flows in one direction. There are two main uses for this current in professional skincare treatments: iontophoresis and desincrustation. Multiple benefits are achieved, including cell stimulation, moving tissue fluid, softening up clogged sebum or comedones, and increasing penetration of active ingredients deep into the epidermis using positive or negative polarity.

Iontophoresis

Using galvanic current on the positive polarity is referred to as "iontophoresis." This polarity is used to help push the appropriate water-soluble active ingredients deeper into the skin for increased effectiveness. Specialty ampoules, serums, masques, and even moisturizers can be used. It is especially beneficial for treating aging skin and discolorations. This positive polarity also has a calming effect, constricting capillaries and reducing irritation and redness which can be beneficial for rosacea and sensitive skin types.

Galvanic on the positive polarity has the following skin effects:

- Acid reaction to balance skin pH
- Tightens and firms tissues
- Constricts the follicles
- Decreases blood flow and sensitivity
- Reduces edema

Desincrustation

Galvanic desincrustation is a process that softens and emulsifies sebum and keratin in the follicle using a negatively charged solution that has been applied to the skin. The appropriate negative electrode is then glided over the skin, resulting in "saponification" or melting of the congested sebum. This safe and gentle procedure is best done during a facial before manual extractions are performed. It allows for much more successful and painless removal of comedones and micro-comedones for congested skin, leaving it very clean.

Galvanic desincrustation has the following effects and benefits:

- An alkaline, skin-softening reaction
- Dilates follicles
- Increases blood and lymph circulation
- Softens compacted sebum and keratin within the follicle
- Attracts negative ions

Before any of the above-mentioned treatments, a thorough consultation with a professionally licensed and trained esthetician should be conducted to determine the most appropriate treatment recommendations along with a supportive home-care regime. It is a partnership between what you do at home (including lifestyle, diet, and nutrition), and the appropriate skincare products that will help you to have beautiful and healthy skin.

SAUNA

WHAT IS SAUNA THERAPY?

Sauna, a Scandinavian word, is an ancient form of dry-heat therapy that has been used around the world by many cultures. It is considered by many to be a cultural and medicinal component of social interaction and health maintenance. Among them are the Mayan sweat lodges, the Mexican temazcal, the Islamic hammam, the Russian banya, the Japanese Mushi-Buro, the Native American sweat lodge, as well as the hot baths described in Indian Ayurvedic medical literature. Ancient Egyptian texts, including the Edwin Smith Papyrus, mention the use of heat therapy for tumors.

Modern science has consistently studied the health effects of saunas for decades and have a very strong case that it can be used in the management of heart-related conditions according to an article published in the *Journal of Cardiology*.

The basic idea of sauna therapy is to heat the body several degrees. The body then attempts to reduce its temperature by driving blood to the surface and by sweating. Saunas dramatically improve circulation and relieve internal congestion. It is also said that heating the body helps destroy bacteria, viruses, and some tumors. In addition, it assists the body in detoxification by ridding harmful toxic metals and chemicals, radioactive particles, and other toxins.

The effects of a sauna session occur in two phases. The first phase, which is usually within the first 10 minutes, induces light sweating and the body temperature remains approximately at a basal level of 98.6.

The body dissipates the extra heat by increasing circulation, shunting blood to the skin surface, and sweating. The benefits of phase one include relaxing the muscles and enhancing the flexibility of tendons and ligaments, pain relief, an overall feeling of relaxation, improving oxygenation and dilating the peripheral blood vessels, and relieving internal organ congestion.

After about 10-to-30 minutes, the body enters phase two. During this phase, the body can no longer dissipate the heat of the sauna and its temperature begins to rise. Some of the greatest benefits occur during this phase. The heart rate and sweating increase and blood is more forcefully shunted to the surface. It increases the heart rate and improves circulation. Also, increasing the body temperature is said to hasten the death of weaker cells as does having a fever when there is infection.

After a sauna session, your body temperature may remain elevated for up to 15 minutes. It is recommended to take a cool shower and rest for 10-to-15 minutes as it allows the body to restore normal functioning.

Saunas may be used for:

- Relaxation and meditation: the warmth of the sauna heat relaxes the muscles and nervous system.
- Health maintenance: weekly sauna sessions enhance circulation, which nourishes the glands, detoxifies the system, cleanses the skin, and offers many of the same benefits received while exercising
- Healing: spending 30 minutes, several days per week, in a sauna is believed to be a very powerful and safe healing modality. It decongests the internal organs, assists circulation, heals infections, and may help other body systems as well.

STEPS TO TAKE A PROPER SAUNA

The sauna is an ancient method of cleansing the body, mind, and soul. It builds up the immune system for overall health. The contrast of hot and cold causes the blood vessels to react quickly to adjust the body temperature to heat or cold. This strengthens the veins and arteries, boosting immunities. In Finnish writings, the sauna is referred to as the Fountain of Youth. The temperature of the sauna room should be at 150-to-160 F.

Proper steps to the perfect sauna experience:

1. Remove all jewelry, as the metal will heat up quickly and can cause burns.

2. Take a light cleansing shower before entering the sauna.
3. Dry brush your skin from your feet to your neck to promote the perspiration process.
4. Remove your robe and enter the sauna, close the door behind you, stand for a moment to adjust your breathing.
5. Remove your slippers and step slowly onto the first bench.
6. Lie down on your towel on the second step. Your head should be slightly elevated on one of the wooden headrests or rolled towel pillows. You want your entire body at the same level without feet hanging below your heart.
7. For your first session, you should set the timer for no longer than eight-to-12 minutes.
8. Relax and drink a glass of water while enjoying the heat.
9. Get up slowly and sit for a moment before standing and exiting the sauna.
10. Enter a shower slowly. Let the water run over your feet, then your legs, hips, and then the entire body.
11. Dry off and rest for 10-to-15 minutes.
12. Repeat for a total of three sauna sessions, cool down, and a resting period.
13. Be sure to replenish lost fluids.
14. Meditation and or a massage following a sauna session is always beneficial.

Sauna therapy is meant to be a relaxing process of transitions between hot and cool. After your final round in the sauna, take some time to cool down once more. Take a cool shower to close your pores and make sure you have stopped sweating before getting dressed.

"There is a tenseness and tautness in the everyday, work-a-day world of Americans, in the hustle-bustle daily drive of making a living. […] It is my contention that Americans should learn to relax more, calm down, quit fighting nature, stop premature aging of the body, and try to eliminate nervous breakdowns. One of the best ways to achieve this is to get into the weekly or semi-weekly, leisurely sauna habit."

—S.C. Olin, Sauna

BEYOND OURSELVES

We all walk through our days carrying huge amounts of stress. And as they say on airplanes, put your own oxygen mask on first. I do believe practicing kindness and caring for ourselves has a ripple effect on our greater communities.

It is also important for me to be connected to a world outside of myself. Whether it is through religious or spiritual practice, a commitment to environmental or social concerns, charitable giving, or caretaking, I believe it is very important to connect and give back.

It is our privilege to serve those around us and taking good care of ourselves allows us to bring our fullest selves to others.

CREATING YOUR HOLISTIC LIFESTYLE

As you've read this book, I hope that something caught your eye and you thought "Yes! I can start this today!" I hope you are empowered to think of your life as opportunities to take better care of yourself and those around you.

Looking back to the self-assessment chart at the beginning of the book, here are some tips for building a holistic, happy life.

Nutritious eating:

- Eating a healthy, nutritious diet
- Drinking plenty of water

Physical activity:

- Daily exercise and movement
- Quality sleep

Fresh air + nature:

- Getting quality time outside daily
- Connecting with nature

Relationships:

- Building and nurturing relationships
- Practicing gratitude and forgiveness

Work:

- Doing work with intention and care
- Practicing kindness and boundaries with coworkers and technology

De-stressing:

- Taking regular breaks from technology
- Creating the time and space to de-stress

Self-care

- Practicing meditation and journaling
- Daily skincare and body care

Professional treatments

- Regular spa visits for massage and facials
- Checkups

There is an old Italian saying: "The best is the enemy of the good." Do not let your expectations that you can only do it if it is "the best" stop you for starting with "the good." Or even "the good enough!"

Unless you are very lucky, it's unlikely that you will have a weeklong retreat to start building your holistic lifestyle. Fortunately, you don't need it. You can start today by incorporating the parts that work best in your life today.

As you begin a new lifestyle, approach these changes with curiosity and joy. Explore new foods you may love, get some fresh air, create a skincare ritual that is enjoyable, and supports your skin health.

Life goes by so quickly; We only have one life to live, I wish only that you can start living your most beautiful life now.

Please keep us posted on your journey. Reach out anytime: hello@duboisbeauty.com.

ABOUT THE AUTHOR

Denise Dubois is the founder of Complexions Spas in Albany and Saratoga Springs, New York. She is also the creator of Dubois Beauty and Wellness, a new line of skincare products that draws from nature with the best clean ingredients to deliver exceptional results.

Denise started her career as an esthetician in 1985 after graduating from the Catherine E. Hinds School of Esthetics — the first accredited esthetics school in the country — where she received the Merretta Gotham Hinds Award for highest achievement.

She has since continued her training and holds several advanced certificates in the following areas of expertise.

- Dermatologic Skin Care
- Medical Esthetics
- Certified Laser Technician
- Microneedling
- Dermaplaning
- Lymphatic Drainage
- IIN Institute of Integrative Nutrition
- Nutritional Skin Care Academy
- Herbology
- Organic cosmetic formulating

MEMBERSHIPS & CERTIFICATIONS

Denise is also an Internationally Certified CIDESCO Diplomat, Esthetics America member, NCEA member, and NY State Representative, Green Spa Network member, ISpa member, Professional Beauty Association member, Day Spa Association member, and NY State Spa Alliance member. She has worked for several board-certified plastic surgeons and dermatologists in the Capital Region and New York City.

Her work includes developing pre- and post-operative skincare programs to optimize plastic surgical results and significantly reduce patient-healing time. She also developed programs for Restorative Youthful Skin, Blemish Control, and Age Management which incorporates nutrition, chemical exfoliation, microdermabrasion, facial treatments, injectables, and laser therapies.

Denise feels strongly that a combination of these modalities truly provides the most beneficial results along with the appropriate home-care regimen. She holds certificates from the Nutritional Skincare Academy and the Science & Art of Herbalism. She is a 2020 graduate of the Institute for Integration Nutrition (INN) and a certified integrated health coach.

OTHER AWARDS & RECOGNITIONS

Denise Dubois has had several articles printed in professional trade journals. She has appeared on local television and radio as well as guest-speaking at professional trade conferences nationally. Complexions Spa for Beauty and Wellness has been recognized by the U.S. Green Building Council as the first Gold LEED-certified spa in the country for new construction, and it received a bronze plaque from NYSERDA for energy efficiency and was Energy Star Small Business of the Year in 2009. Green Spa Network awarded Complexions Spa for Beauty & Wellness as Best Green Day Spa of the year in 2017.

ADDITIONAL RESOURCES

Continue your wellness journey with great organizations and online resources.

- Institute for Integrative Nutrition: https://www.integrativenutrition.com/

- Nutritional Skincare Academy: https://www.nutritionalskincareacademy.com/

- The Center for Mindful Eating: https://thecenterformindfuleating.org/

- Dr. Mark Hyman: https://drhyman.com

- Japanese Bathing, from the Association of Nature and Forest Therapy Guides and Programs: http://www.shinrin-yoku.org/

- Environmental Working Group: https://www.ewg.org/

- *Vitamin A Skin Science* by Dr. Des Fernandez and Dr. Ernst Eiselen,